Photograph by Aerofilms Ltd.

Frontispiece. Southport and the Ribble Estuary.

AGRICULTURAL RESEARCH COUNCIL

Memoirs of the Soil Survey of Great Britain
England and Wales

Soils of the
OUTH-WEST LANCASHIRE
COASTAL PLAIN

[SHEETS 74 and 83]

B. R. HALL and C. J. FOLLAND

HARPENDEN
1967

To be purchased from
the Librarian
Rothamsted Experimental Station
Harpenden, Herts.

Printed in England by
ADLARD AND SON LIMITED
BARTHOLOMEW PRESS, DORKING

PREFACE

This memoir describes the soils of the coastal plain between Blackpool and Liverpool which, although small in extent, is highly productive of a variety of valuable horticultural and agricultural crops. The work is an extension of the mapping done on the adjacent 3rd Edition Sheet 75 (Preston) and some of the soils are the same as those described in the memoir accompanying that map.

The problems confronting the community, however, are different for the management of the water regime of productive farm land, made from mossland and ill-drained sandy soils, necessitates the provision of costly and extensive drainage works which bring their own difficulties. Other problems with entirely different characters are presented in the reclamation of land for grazing in the Ribble estuary.

The survey, started in 1956 under the direction of the late Dr. A. Muir, was made by B. R. Hall with some assistance from C. W. Montgomery. C. L. Bascomb is responsible for the analytical data and the maps and diagrams were prepared under the guidance of E. M. Thomson.

It is a pleasure to acknowledge the contribution to the section on climate made by Mr. J. A. Taylor of the University College of Wales, Aberystwyth and also by the Meteorological Office (Tables 1–6 and Fig. 6). The section on contemporary agriculture was provided by Messrs. J. K. Thompson, A. J. H. West and B. P. Richardson of the National Agricultural Advisory Service while Mr. J. Webber, Advisory Soil Chemist for Yorkshire and Lancashire, supplied data relating to the organic soils; Mr. J. A. Haywood, County Horticultural Officer, contributed the section on horticulture. The Survey is grateful to these officers for the assistance willingly given. D. V. Stewart of the University College of Wales, Aberystwyth is thanked for co-operation in the collection of ecological data.

The authors wish to acknowledge the help of Mr. J. F. B. Tew, Agricultural Land Service, and Dr. R. K. Gresswell, Liverpool University, in giving information used in discussing the land use and geomorphology. B. W. Avery is thanked for permission to quote from his memoir on the soils of the district around Aylesbury and Hemel Hempstead.

Finally, the survey could not have been made without the permission of the farmers and land-owners to inspect their land; permission was always willingly given and the Survey is grateful for their co-operation.

Copies of the one-inch coloured soil maps are obtainable from Ordnance Survey agents. Fair copies of the field sheets are kept at the headquarters of the Soil Survey where they can be inspected by appointment.

D. A. OSMOND
Head of the Soil Survey of England and Wales

31*st March* 1966
Rothamsted Experimental Station,
Harpenden, Herts.

CONTENTS

TEXT FIGURES

PLATES

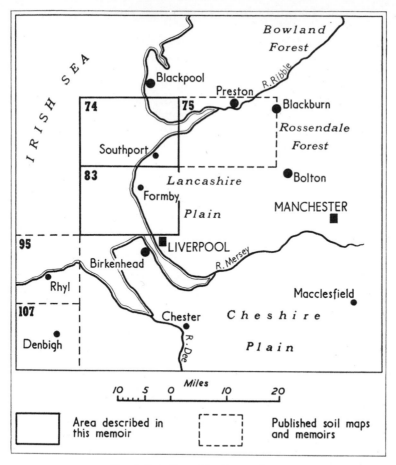

Fig. 1. Location of the Survey Area.

CHAPTER I

General Description of the Area

The district consists of part of the western edge of the coastal plain of south-west Lancashire and is bounded by the northern suburbs of Liverpool in the south, by Blackpool in the north, by the sea in the west, and by a north–south line through the Clieves Hills in the east (Fig. 1). The district is low-lying and is divided by the wide estuary of the Ribble so that of the total area of 432 sq. miles only 110 sq. miles lie above the high-water mark of ordinary tides, the remainder consisting of tidal flats of sand and mud.

With the exception of the industrial regions in the south and the coastal resorts, the district is predominantly agricultural and the close proximity of very highly populated towns provides a ready market for farm and market-garden produce. The production of high quality crops of cereals, roots and vegetables is encouraged by the presence of easily worked soils suitable for intensive cultivation and an evenly distributed annual rainfall of about 35 in.

1

Between the extensive suburbs of Liverpool and Blackpool the main towns are Southport, which, with Birkdale and Ainsdale, has a population of approximately 85,000, Lytham St. Anne's (30,000) and Formby (10,000). Southport and Lytham St. Anne's (Fig. 2 and 8) are two of the most important holiday resorts in the north-west of England and are very dependent on the seasonal tourist trade. Attractive villages, including Scarisbrick, Halsall, Haskayne, Aughton and Westby, and smaller hamlets are situated to the east. Settlements on the intervening mossland are sparse, usually isolated farmhouses sited on ridges and hummocks of clay protruding through the peat. The mossland and the Ribble estuary are barriers to communications and south of the Ribble the main roads and railways run approximately from north to south skirting these great areas of peat which are traversed only by secondary roads and the Southport–Manchester railway. North of the Ribble, east–west communications link Lytham St. Anne's and Blackpool with Preston and east Lancashire.

PHYSICAL FEATURES

The district comprises part of the flat coast north of Liverpool and the south-western part of the low-lying land between the Ribble and the Wyre known as the Fylde. The land rises gradually from sea-level in the west to reach a maximum elevation of 175 ft. O.D. on the Clieves Hills. Much of the district lies below 25 ft. and land over 75 ft. is of small extent (Fig. 3).

An extensive formation of stable and unstable dunes with excellent examples of slacks, swales and flat links sand borders the coast between Blackpool and Lytham St. Anne's and between Southport and Crosby (*Plate II*). The broad estuary of the Ribble forms the southern boundary of the Fylde and extensive salt marshes are well developed along it north-east of Southport. Embankments were constructed in the late 19th century when small-scale reclamation of the marshes was successfully carried out.

Well-known sandy beaches stretch along the coast south of the Ribble, and deposits of sand blown from them and the dunes reach their maximum width at Formby where there are also wide flat sandy areas. The sands form the western edge of the extensive and monotonously flat area of peat or mossland which occurs between the dunes and the slightly higher land to the east. The peat extends in a broad crescent northward from near Maghull through Great Altcar, where it is approximately three miles wide, to Southport, where it adjoins Martin Mere and merges into the mossland between Southport and Rufford. Most of the mossland lies between 12 and 15 ft. O.D.; nowhere does it rise above 25 ft. O.D. and the surface is gradually being lowered by the continual shrinkage and wastage of the peat. Hedges are rare since all fields are bounded by open ditches, leading excess drainage water into embanked channels which eventually take it either into the Alt or into Crossens Pool whence it is pumped into the sea. The removal of water is difficult because of the very low gradients and the continuous lowering of the surface in an area only slightly above sea-level.

North of the Ribble where the peat occupies valley bottoms, mossland is less extensive. The occurrence of pronounced ridges and knolls of boulder clay separating peat-filled, flat-bottomed valleys forms a landscape that is quite different from the extensive flats south of the Ribble.

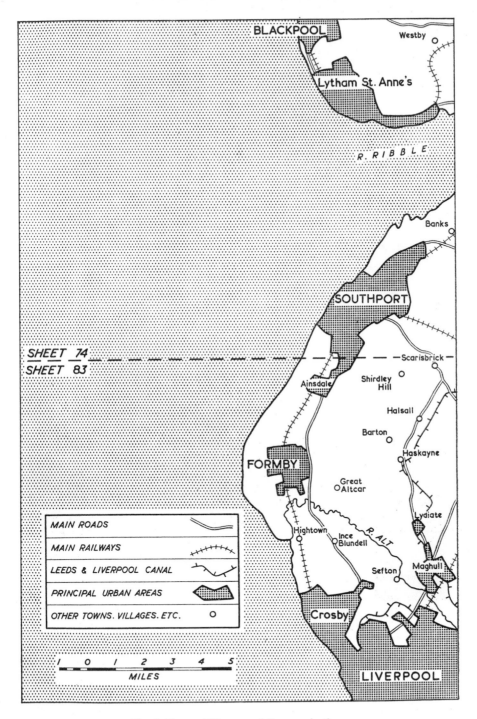

Fig. 2. Towns, Villages and Communications.

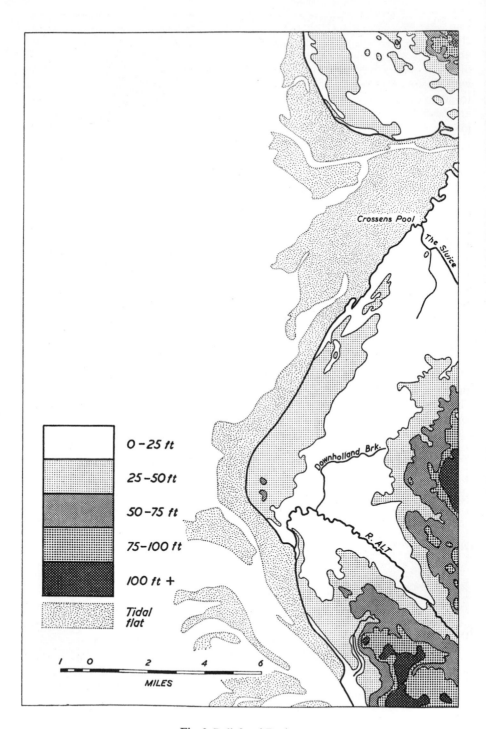

Fig. 3. Relief and Drainage.

The eastern boundary of the mossland south of the Ribble is marked by a sharp rise at about the 25-foot contour-line, to the east of which the land lies chiefly between 25 ft. and 75 ft. although beyond Downholland Cross it rises abruptly to a maximum of 175 ft. O.D. on the Clieves Hills. The landscape is one of broad undulations and depressions in the boulder clay which is thinly covered with Shirdley Hill Sand, and through which small outcrops of sandstone protrude to give rise to more upstanding hillocks and ridges. It is traversed by the Alt and between Ince Blundell and Crosby, south and west of the river, sandstone hillocks are of more common occurrence.

The Alt flows north-west from its source near Huyton but south of Formby it turns in a wide loop to flow southward and enter the sea near Hightown. Between Ince Blundell and Formby the river flows across a flat, delta-shaped, stretch of alluvium that is extremely wide for such a small river. The calcareous nature of the deposit suggests that tidal flooding was extensive before it was prevented by the formation of sand dunes. It has been suggested that the alluvium represents the delta of the Alt laid down when the Hillhouse Coastline was the most westerly extent of the land (Gresswell, *priv. com.*). The district is further drained by small, westward flowing streams in narrow valleys that drain into the peat areas and eventually reach the Alt or Crossens Pool. Rimrose brook takes the water from around Thornton south-west into the Mersey estuary. Wider, flat-bottomed and peat-filled valleys with only minor streams are common north of the Ribble.

GEOLOGY

Most of the district is covered by deposits of Pleistocene and more recent age and exposures of the underlying solid geological formations are uncommon. The formations represented are given in the following table, the only solid formations exposed being of Triassic rocks (Wray and Cope, 1948).

Drift or Superficial Deposits

Recent and Post-glacial	Blown Sand
	Freshwater and Estuarine Alluvium
	Peat
	Downholland Silt
	Shirdley Hill Sand*
Glacial	Upper Boulder Clay
	Middle Sands
	Lower Boulder Clay

Solid Formations (Triassic)

Keuper	Keuper Marl
	Keuper Waterstones
	Keuper Sandstone
Bunter	Upper Mottled Sandstone
	Pebble Beds
	Lower Mottled Sandstone

* Although Shirdley Hill Sand is generally recognized as the oldest Post-glacial deposit thin bands of peat may occur between it and the underlying till.

Triassic Rocks

The solid rocks exposed, or which lie immediately beneath the superficial deposits, are all marls and sandstones of Triassic age. The regional dip of the rocks ranges between north and north-west, the inclination varying between the horizontal and 10°. As a result the lower and somewhat more resistant members of the succession (Bunter and Keuper sandstones) crop out in the south-east (Wray and Cope, 1948).

The Bunter Formation of red, yellow, and mottled sandstones, underlies the south and south-east part of the district. Further sub-divisions into the Upper and Lower Mottled Sandstones, and Pebble Beds are not shown on the Geological Survey maps partly because of the lack of exposures owing to the thick cover of superficial deposits but also because they cannot be distinguished in the absence of the Pebble Beds which occur infrequently. The most extensive outcrop of the Formation is at Melling where it gives rise to an upstanding hillock on which Melling Church stands.

The rocks of the overlying Keuper Formation are different in character and the Keuper Sandstone is harder, coarser and less homogeneous than the Bunter Sandstone. Outcrops of the Keuper Sandstone are more frequent than of the underlying Bunter Sandstone and are similarly confined to the south of the Ribble. The colour of the sandstone is variable and may be greenish yellow or dull red and bands of marl are not infrequent. Keuper Sandstone forms the Clieves Hills, the highest land in the district, but notable outcrops also occur at Ince Blundell, Thornton and at Hillhouse, together with other small exposures around Haskayne.

It is probable that Keuper Marl underlies the whole of the district north and west of Blundellsands, Ince Blundell, Hillhouse, Barton and Halsall. The greatest thickness recorded is 971 ft. at Great Altcar but east of Blackpool the total thickness may well exceed 2,000 ft. (Wray and Cope, 1948). The beds consist of greyish green and reddish-coloured clays with numerous intercalated bands of flaggy and marly sandstone. The marl is exposed only at Clay Brow Farm, south of Brown Edge, where it gives rise to a low hillock partially covered by boulder clay.

Drift Deposits and Landscape Development

Most of the Lancashire plain is covered by Glacial, Post-glacial and Recent deposits and for a better understanding of the relationships between them a brief discussion of geological events during and after the Pleistocene glaciation is necessary. Fig. 4 is a sketch map of the distribution of the deposits and the subject is admirably treated by Gresswell (1953).

During the Pleistocene era the entire district was covered with ice which had moved into the Lancashire plain across the Irish Sea from the Lake District and the Southern Uplands of Scotland. The retreat of the ice exposed a vast plain covered with boulder clay (till). This is a reddish brown silty clay derived largely from Triassic rocks with a few rounded pebbles incorporated. The pebbles originate from the Lake District and Scotland and prove the dominantly southern movement of the ice. In other parts of England there is evidence of the advance and retreat of more than one ice sheet but in this district such evidence is lacking although the possibility of an interglacial period cannot be ignored.

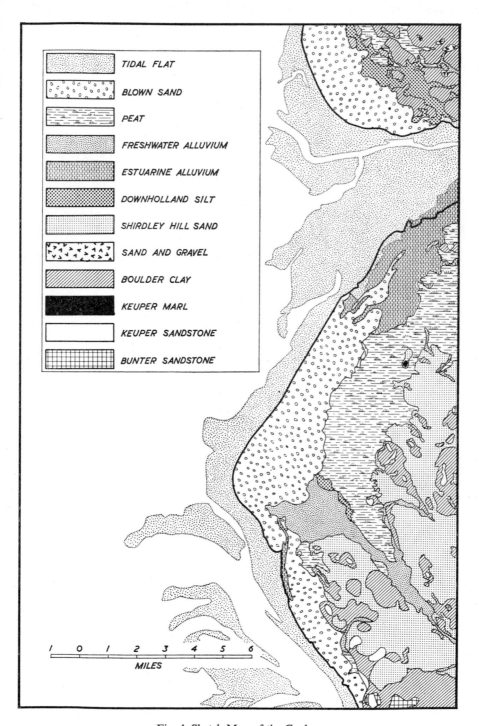

Fig. 4. Sketch Map of the Geology.

Even though the ice melted from the region of the Irish Sea at the close of the Glacial Period, there was a general world shortage of oceanic water because of the extensive ice sheets elsewhere. The coastline of the boulder clay plain in the immediate Post-glacial period, therefore, lay far west of the present one and was probably near the present 20-fathom contour (De Rance, 1883). Continuing thaw elsewhere increased the volume of water in the oceans which, in conjunction with the normal marine erosion of the boulder clay, resulted in a slow eastward migration of the coastline to the approximate position of the present 25-foot contour-line where it is now visible as a line of low cliffs between Hillhouse and Shirdley Hill (Stage 1 in Fig. 5). This coastline, referred to as the Hillhouse Coastline, corresponds to the 25-foot raised beach in Scotland and is thought to date from about 5000 B.C., the time of the Flandrian transgression in other parts of the world. Data derived from pollen analysis of similar sites in the Furness district of north Lancashire indicates that the transgression occurred between the periods of pollen zones VI and VIIa, commonly known as the Boreal–Atlantic transition (Gresswell, 1958).

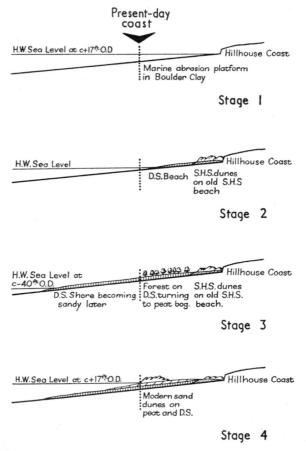

Fig. 5. Diagrammatic Sections illustrating the Development of the Coastal Plain (from *Sandy Shores in South Lancashire* by permission of Dr. Kay Gresswell and the University of Liverpool Press).

As a consequence of the removal of the weight of ice, the land began to rise, the sea retreated westwards and a beach, sandy near the cliffs but muddy nearer the sea, was formed (Stage 2). The sand now known as Shirdley Hill Sand, built up against the low cliffs and was subsequently blown inland by westerly winds. Undulations in the surface of the boulder clay were almost completely obliterated by sheets of blown sand of variable thickness. The sand was often carried a considerable distance and has been recorded, for example, on Billinge Hill at approximately 400 ft. O.D., twelve miles east of the Hillhouse Coastline. Nearer the Coastline it is recorded as extending from Gore House nearly to Scarisbrick in the form of the original sandy beach beneath the peat through which it occasionally protrudes in low dune-like mounds.

The fine-textured part of the beach, now known as the Downholland Silt and locally referred to as "Scotch" or "Blue Billy", typically consists of silty clays, pale blue in colour when fresh, but grey, cream or brown when weathered. In general the thickness varies between 5 and 10 ft. but deep borings have shown it to be between 30 and 50 ft. thick in places. It contains complete and fragmented marine, estuarine and freshwater shells indicating it was possibly laid down in the lagoons that typically develop on an emerging coast.

At a later period the beach of Downholland Silt was colonized by vegetation in which birch, alder and oak appear to have been dominant. Deterioration of the drainage, due to the low gradients, the occurrence of temporary dunes and ridges and, probably, a climatic change, led to the death of the trees and the formation of reed swamp peat in the swampy basin sites (Stage 3 in Fig. 5).

Peat deposits occupy a greater area than any other formation on the Southport and Formby sheets. They occur on the seaward side of the Hillhouse Coastline and extend from Hesketh Bank to Crosby although covered by blown sand and estuarine alluvium near the present coast. North of the Ribble peat occurs extensively in the numerous flat-bottomed valleys between Blackpool and Kirkham. It normally rests directly on the Downholland Silt but overlies Shirdley Hill Sand immediately west of the Hillhouse Coastline south of the Ribble (Fig. 7, p. 74). Borings made during the survey show that the average thickness of the peat is about 6 ft. although it may be up to 20 ft. in places.

Recent Deposits

Deposits younger than the peat include river and estuarine alluvium and blown sand. The prevailing westerly winds have caused the formation of the extensive belt of blown sand along the present coast both north and south of the Ribble. Erosion of the dunes at Formby Point appears to have started about 1906, and is now occurring on a front three miles wide at a mean rate of about 24 ft. per annum. At the same time, there is accretion between Southport and Ainsdale and north of Hightown, due partly to north-easterly and south-westerly migration of beach material away from Formby Point.

Bordering the Ribble estuary is a wide tract of estuarine alluvium composed of laminated silts and fine sand with numerous complete and fragmented shells. Freshwater alluvium is confined to the river valleys, particularly that of the Alt. The Alt alluvium consists of laminated brown silt and sand with grey sandy clay and is underlain by Downholland Silt, peat or sand and gravel. Unlike the estuarine alluvium it does not contain shells and has a much smaller content of calcium carbonate.

2

CLIMATE

Macro-climate

In general terms the south-west Lancashire coastlands have a conspicuously maritime climate and are accessible to air derived from the north-west whilst being sheltered from east and north-east winds.

In broad terms the average seasonal sequence is a cool, wet, winter with but little snow, a relatively dry spring and a summer becoming progressively, but intermittently, warmer succeeded by a warm, and often wet, late summer and autumn. The Irish Sea is a major influence in determining the climate of the district particularly near the coast. Off Southport and Blackpool average sea-surface temperatures reach a maximum of about 61°F. in August and a minimum of about 41°F. in February (Bowden, 1953). The effect on the coastlands is that winter minimum temperatures are relatively high, summer minimum temperatures are relatively lower and the climate is equable. These effects become less pronounced towards the east away from the coast until increasing elevation depresses both maximum and minimum temperatures. Neither average temperature nor average rainfall figures show much variation except a slight increase in summer of 1–2°F. with distance south of Southport, and a slight increase in rainfall with distance to the north and east (Fig. 6). The rain-shadow cast over

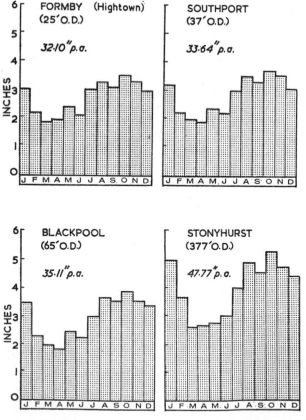

Fig. 6. Rainfall at Four Localities (Meteorological Office, 1958).

Merseyside by the high land of North Wales becomes less pronounced northward from Liverpool and the consistently low altitude of the immediate hinterlands of Southport and Blackpool maintains the low rainfall of the coast. Distribution of average numbers of rain days (Table 1), i.e. days with at least 0·01 in. of rain, shows little variation.

Snow is not often seen; for example at Southport, during the period 1920–1949, snow fell on 12·9 days and days with snow lying numbered 5·6.

TABLE 1

Distribution of Average Number of Rain Days

	J	F	M	A	M	J	J	A	S	O	N	D	Year
Blackpool	20	16	17	15	15	13	15	18	15	19	19	22	204
Southport	18	16	16	15	15	13	15	18	14	18	18	21	197
Stonyhurst	21	16	17	15	16	14	16	20	15	19	19	21	209

As can be seen from Table 2 humidity at the coast is high compared with inland. Calculations of losses of moisture by evaporation (Table 3) and of the irrigation-need indicate that moisture deficiency in the soil is rare and that the frequency of irrigation-need is less than 5 years in 10 and decreases northward from the southern districts near Liverpool.

TABLE 2

Estimated Average Percentage Relative Humidities
(*at* 1300 *hrs.*)

	J	F	M	A	M	J	J	A	S	O	N	D	Year
(A)	85	80	70	70	65	70	70	70	75	75	80	85	75
(B)	80	75	70	65	60	60	65	65	70	70	80	80	70

(A) data for the coastal area; (B) data for the immediate inland.

Of the strong and moderate winds at Southport and Blackpool (Baxendell, 1935) those with a westerly component are more frequent than those with an easterly component though this does not apply to winds of less than 4 knots. The decrease of wind speed with distance from the sea is less than the average; the wind speed on the coast is 13·0 m.p.h. and only falls to 12·5 m.p.h. at the eastern edge of the district. Average annual gale frequencies, however, decrease from about 18 days on the coast to about 12 days inland (Meteorological Office, 1952); gales are commonest between October and March.

Land and sea breezes are normally well developed especially in summer when sea breezes may penetrate and pass beyond the whole district. The wide expanse of the dunes and the sandy foreshores enhances the temperature contrast between air over the land and over the sea, and intensifies land and sea breezes.

Sunshine data suggest a very slight decrease northward in average annual sunshine duration although the southern parts of the district must suffer a

TABLE 3

Evaporation Figures for Southport 1941–50 (in.)*

	J	F	M	A	M	J	J	A	S	O	N	D	Year
1941	0·00	0·14	0·68	1·36	2·11	3·14	3·43	2·40	1·07	0·77	0·18	0·16	15·44
1942	0·00	(0·10)	0·50	2·18	2·79	3·99	3·23	1·70	1·93	0·87	0·48	0·33	18·10
1943	0·13	0·54	1·10	2·03	2·61	3·10	3·74	2·53	1·82	0·86	0·44	0·14	19·04
1944	0·10	0·15	0·50	1·60	2·21	2·44	2·35	2·37	1·30	0·54	0·31	0·03	13·90
1945	(0·15)	0·27	0·74	1·66	2·00	3·08	2·69	2·23	1·24	0·68	0·26	0·20	15·20
1946	0·14	0·34	0·56	1·47	3·03	(2·38)	3·14	2·30	1·12	0·80	0·03C	0·03C	(15·31)
1947	0·26	0·44	0·53	1·37	1·90	2·58	2·44	2·90	1·32	0·43	0·36	0·05	14·58
1948	0·26	0·34	0·80	1·29	2·69	2·40	2·60	1·62	0·85	0·33	0·09	0·09	13·36
1949	0·08	0·04	0·42	1·42	2·69	3·23	3·45	2·36	1·21	0·92	0·29	0·11	16·22
1950	0·04	0·11	0·56	1·35	2·23	2·97	3·04	2·69	1·26	0·68	0·12	0·12	15·17
Av.	0·09	0·20	0·53	1·31	2·02	2·44	2·51	1·43	1·09	0·57	0·21	0·10	13·02

* Figures in brackets are estimated, C indicates condensation.

TABLE 4

Gales at Southport

(*Periods* 1913–37, 1898–1912)

	J	F	M	A	M	J	J	A	S	O	N	D	Year
Mean number of days (1913–37)	3	2	2	0·9	0·6	0·7	0·5	0·7	1	2	2	3	19
Mean number of hours (1913–37)	19	10	11	4	2	3	3	3	7	13	14	17	106
Average highest gust in knots (1898–1912)	68	61	57	56	50	50	59	49	55	62	64	63	79
Highest recorded gust in knots (1898–1912)	89	86	80	80	72	63	66	72	90	96	87	88	96

reduction from the occasional northward drift of industrial pollution from Merseyside. At Southport, sea fogs occur, on an average, on 21 mornings per annum, drifting in with the sea breezes and somewhat reducing the amounts of sunshine.

TABLE 5

Average Duration of Bright Sunshine in Hours

(*Period* 1921–1950)

	J	F	M	A	M	J	J	A	S	O	N	D	Year
Southport 31 ft. O.D.	44	66	119	166	206	217	185	173	132	98	54	38	1498
Blackpool 65 ft. O.D.	44	66	117	164	207	213	182	170	130	96	54	37	1480
Bolton 350 ft. O.D.	23	41	77	117	164	178	149	140	98	71	35	19	1112
Stonyhurst 377 ft. O.D.	39	55	102	140	188	190	159	152	117	87	50	34	1313
Darwen 730 ft. O.D.	31	47	94	128	173	180	150	146	105	77	43	22	1196

The Growing Season

The average date for the last "screen" frost is not later than April 15th on the immediate coastlands; east and north-east towards Preston it is after May 1st. Average dates of first "screen" frost show a similar range from after November 15th on the coast to before November 1st inland to the north-east.

The average mean daily temperature (reduced to sea-level) rises above 42°F. (a threshold temperature below which, *cet. par.*, plants make little growth) on about February 26th in the south-west and on about March 3rd in the north-east, indicating the general northward and north-eastward decrease in onset of growth across south-west Lancashire. Isophenes or lines of equal average flowering dates of selected plants range from about May 9th in the south-east to about May 13th in the north-east. In general, the area is considered early by national standards when the northerly latitude is considered.

Micro-climate

By contrast with the relative uniformity of the macro-climate, the micro-climate shows considerable variation as a result of the distribution of extremely contrasted surface deposits.

Ground frost at Southport, 31 ft. O.D. and on the coast, is on the average as frequent as at Stonyhurst 377 ft. O.D., and more frequent than at Bolton 342 ft. O.D., both some 24 miles inland. Truly representative maritime conditions are reproduced only at Holyhead.

TABLE 6

Mean Number of Days with Ground Frost

(*Period* 1920–1949)

	J	F	M	A	M	J	J	A	S	O	N	D	Year
Southport	11·7	10·8	11·4	6·6	3·4	0·4	0·0	0·0	1·0	4·6	7·4	10·2	67·5
Stonyhurst	13·0	12·1	11·3	6·3	2·6	0·1	0·0	0·0	0·4	2·8	8·0	10·8	67·4
Bolton	13·2	10·4	10·6	4·7	1·7	0·0	0·0	0·0	0·1	2·1	7·7	10·6	61·1
Holyhead	5·0	5·8	5·9	1·7	1·0	0·1	0·0	0·0	0·0	0·6	2·4	3·4	25·9

The relatively high local frequency of ground frosts on the land around Southport and elsewhere along the south Lancashire coast is due to the sandy nature of the soils. On higher ground to the east, however, ground frosts are an expression of the low temperature of the air. On many lowland sites they are more often due to the accumulation of cold air in basins or on flat land usually on calm, clear nights. The surface morphology of the sand dunes along the coast presents a range of slope and aspect providing examples of both good and bad air drainage. Potential small frost pockets abound in the peaty slacks but the very high ground-water table tends to reduce frost incidence. On the landward side of the dunes, cold air on clear, calm nights may, on occasion, gravitate inland locally on to the peat land. The exposures of Keuper Sandstone (*e.g.* at Clieves Hills) coincide with the local high ground which also has good air drainage. The boulder clays, too, dominate the convexities in the ground surface and thus their relatively low liability to frost is reinforced by relief. The Shirdley Hill Sand country is more broadly undulating and, although hollows and flat areas are potential frost pockets, cold air may gravitate extensively from it on clear, calm nights to adjacent peat areas.

Climatic Conditions of the Organic Soils

The large expanses of organic soils warrant separate consideration of their peculiar climatic regime and the problems involved. All the land concerned is at a low elevation and is affected by the gravitational drift of cold air from adjacent higher ground. Peat has a high water-holding capacity and normally the moss-land is wet at or near the surface for long periods of the year with water frequently standing in the open ditches while the vegetation, particularly in winter and spring, is often wet. The immobility of most of the water held within the plant remains and the relative stagnation of drainage water in winter and spring, together with the extremely low thermal conductivity result in very limited penetration of solar heat into the peat. The dark colour of the peat, however, renders it a better absorber of heat than lighter-coloured mineral soils, so that a narrow zone, comprising the air just above the ground-surface and the peat immediately below, can become excessively heated by the sun and suffer violent fluctuations of temperature. These fluctuations die out rapidly within the first few feet of the air above the ground-surface and, much more rapidly than in sandy soils, in the peat below it. Evaporation of the excessive moisture contained in these organic soils reduces the surface temperature but the effect is somewhat offset by the layer of moist air, characteristic of peat land, which tends to reduce heat losses by absorption.

The effects of these interacting phenomena vary with the season. In spring (March–April), when the angle of the sun is low, the mossland is wet and, even at mid-day, the air just above ground is generally humid. Under these conditions absorption of solar heat, even by the dark-coloured peat, is ineffective in warming the soil and radiant energy is dissipated in evaporating surface moisture, with the consequent tendency for the temperature to be reduced. The net result is low night minimum temperatures and a high incidence of frost at the ground surface or in the air layer just above it. The land, therefore, is "late" from the farming viewpoint not only because of its wetness but because this also contributes to its slow response to the early spring sun.

By early summer (May–June) the sun is higher so that the dark-coloured ground is more effectively warmed. Both ground and vegetation are drier and the air just above the ground is less humid at mid-day. However, heat exchange is still limited to the top few inches of soil and deeper layers are only slowly affected. After dry, sunny afternoons, evaporation may be sufficiently intense to affect plant growth and to increase the possibility of late killing frosts.

During July, August and September, the cumulative effect of the rising temperature affects the whole profile which is at a substantially higher temperature than earlier in the year although the diurnal range at depth is still small. The surface of the peat and, during the day, the layer of air above it are at their driest while drainage water is less in quantity and is more mobile. Under these conditions, maximum daytime heating is encouraged whilst at night the tendency for the humidity of the air layer to rise tends to reduce the loss of heat. Furthermore, because the ground is drier there is less evaporation and the loss of heat from this cause is reduced. Plant growth during late June, July and August is therefore remarkably accelerated and crops, planted two to four weeks later than those on adjacent mineral soils, are able to compensate substantially for the late planting. Harvests, however, are usually a week or so later on the peat despite the accelerated growth because the period of maximum growth coincides with the shorter length of day. The intensification of chemical and micro-biological activity is retarded which delays the maturing of crops rather more than their growth. This is particularly true of grain and root crops but not of brassicas where vegetative growth is the aim of production.

By September and later in the autumn, the lower sun, the wetter ground surface, the increasing evaporation and the persistance of more humid air layers reduce the net gain of heat. In the deeper layers of the soil the accumulated summer warmth is still effective so that the onset of autumnal conditions is relatively retarded and the mossland is, therefore, suitable for late cropping.

The coldest part of the winter occurs in February rather than January and prepares the way for the late spring of the next growing season.

The net result is that mossland farms are about two to four weeks later in starting the season and a fortnight later in harvest than farms on sandy soils, the delay being approximately equivalent to a difference in altitude of some 700 ft. or, a distance from the sea of some 200 miles.

It is evident that the topographic uniformity of the south-west Lancashire plain is in sharp contrast with wide variations in both season and productivity due, fundamentally, to differences between the soils.

CHAPTER II

Soil Formation, Classification and Mapping

SOIL FORMATION

The formation and evolution of soils involves three main groups of processes, namely (1) addition and decay of organic residues; (2) physical and chemical weathering of the original rock material; (3) redistribution of soluble or finely dispersed constituents by soil–water movements.

(1) Wherever the ground is stabilized beneath a cover of vegetation, plant remains are continually being added to the surface and sub-surface layers, either directly or through animals, and form sources of food and energy for an interdependent population of soil-inhabiting organisms. Part of the organic material added to the soil normally undergoes oxidative decomposition (mineralization), with the result that parts of the contained nitrogen and mineral nutrients become available to nourish successive generations of plants, while parts are transformed into dark-coloured humus which becomes more or less incorporated with the mineral particles and decomposes at a much slower rate. The amount of organic matter accumulated in or on the soil represents the balance between addition of residues and losses by mineralization, which is governed in turn by the nature of the vegetation, and by various environmental factors, including moisture conditions, aeration, temperature, and nutrient supply, which regulate the composition and activity of the soil population.

(2) The mineral particles of the soil are also subject to more gradual disintegration and decomposition and, through these weathering processes, nutrient elements are released in forms available to plants. Except in the initial stages of soil formation on hard rocks where physical break-down predominates, the prime agent of weathering is rain-water charged with oxygen and carbon dioxide. As this acidulated water percolates through the soil it causes various reactions to take place at the surface of mineral particles; thus, fragments of chalk or limestone are gradually dissolved; micas and other minerals in sedimentary rocks take up water to form more hydrated minerals; ferrous and sulphide ions are oxidized; and primary silicate minerals such as feldspar are hydrolized, whereby alkali and alkaline-earth cations and silica pass into solution. The rates of decomposition vary greatly with the size and constitution of the particles, but normally increase with the quantity and temperature of the percolating water.

(3) Wherever the annual rainfall exceeds evaporation, soluble products of weathering are removed in the drainage water, whilst other products, including clay minerals and hydrated ferric oxides, tend to accumulate, together with quartz and other resistant minerals inherited from the parent rock. The principal cations, calcium, magnesium, potassium and sodium, can be held in exchangeable form on the surface of clay and humus particles after being set free, but are relatively easily removed by continual leaching. so that unless they can be replaced as a result of the weathering of less soluble minerals the soil tends to

become acid in reaction. Clay minerals and other finely dispersed weathering products are translocated downwards under certain conditions, but are generally redeposited in sub-surface horizons, where they are held either in fine pores and fissures or are deposited by coagulation and drying on the surfaces of larger particles.

Restricted drainage, by hindering or preventing removal of decomposition products affects the type and intensity of weathering and leads in particular to the prevalence of reducing processes. Well drained soils are normally freely aerated, so that oxidizing conditions predominate, but where water stagnates in the soil for appreciable periods micro-organisms and plant roots use the dissolved oxygen faster than it can be renewed. Under such anaerobic conditions, accessible ferric ions are reduced to the ferrous state, either by microbial action or by direct reaction with soluble products of plant decomposition (Bloomfield, 1951). This process, known as gleying, results in the development of grey colours in contrast to the characteristic browns and reds of ferric oxides formed in well drained soils by oxidative weathering. As the reduced iron compounds are relatively soluble, they tend to migrate, either in seepage water or by capillary diffusion, towards dryer zones and, where waterlogging is intermittent, are commonly reoxidized to form ochreous deposits or concentrations which impart a mottled appearance to the layers concerned. Manganese behaves similarly and is redeposited as manganese dioxide in seasonally waterlogged soils.

The weathering and translocation processes affecting the inorganic fraction of the soil are intensified to varying degrees by the solvent action of organic acids and other compounds derived from plant residues. Concurrently, however, roots are continually removing from the subsoil nutrient elements and other products of weathering, including silica, which become incorporated in leaves and stems that are eventually returned to the surface. The vegetation thus produces a continuous circulation of mineral substances in the soil, and counteracts, to some extent, their removal by leaching. In many soils earthworms and other burrowing animals also bring material to the surface and so, in effect, oppose the process of removal.

The Soil Profile

The continual interaction of these processes is reflected in the differentiation of more or less distinct *soil horizons*, roughly parallel to the ground surface, which may differ from each other in such features as colour, texture, structure, type and amount of organic matter, degree of root development, or faunal activity. The whole system of layers lying within the zone penetrated by plant roots constitutes the *soil profile*, and the material in which the soil horizons have developed is termed the parent material. The relatively unaltered material below can sometimes be regarded as equivalent to the parent material; commonly, however, the soil horizons appear either to have developed in material different from that lying immediately below, or to be superimposed on a vertical succession of differing materials.

SOIL SURVEY METHODS

In order to describe or to map the soils of a given area, it is necessary to adopt some form of classification. Although soils may be classified in many different ways, all modern systems of classification and mapping recognize the soil profile as the unit of study. In making a soil survey, profiles are examined in pits, auger borings and exposed sections, and information is assembled on relationships between soil properties and other features of the terrain, including land-form, vegetation and geology. On the basis of these observations the soils are grouped into mapping units, each characterized by a limited and defined range of profile variation.

The principal mapping unit used in England and Wales for detailed surveys is the *soil series*, defined as a group of soils having the same or similar succession of horizons in the profile, developed in lithologically similar parent material. In establishing soil series, emphasis is given to relatively permanent features of the profile, such as mechanical composition and subsoil characteristics, and not to more ephemeral features as nutrient status, pH and organic-matter content that may be altered by fertilization, liming and other cultural practices. It will be appreciated, therefore, that when an area of a given series has remained under semi-natural vegetation while another has been cultivated more or less intensively for long periods, the upper horizons in particular will differ considerably in both morphology and constitution. The immediate productivity of soils may also vary widely, depending on recent management history, but areas of the same series should present similar problems in management, and respond similarly to weather conditions and cultural practices.

Each established soil series is named from the locality where it was first described or is well represented. When appreciable variations in surface texture occur within a series, subdivisions (sometimes referred to as *soil types*) may be distinguished. Other subdivisions based on such features as thickness of horizons (including depth to bedrock) or degree of slope are referred to as *phases* (*e.g.* deep phase, steep phase).

Once the main mapping units have been established by a preliminary reconnaissance, their boundaries are determined by boring at frequent intervals with a three-foot auger, and plotted on O.S. maps at the scale of 1 : 10,560 (6 in. to 1 mile). The sites of each boring and profile pit are also recorded, using appropriate symbols to indicate soil series, surface texture, stoniness, degree of slope and subsoil features. In rolling or hilly landscapes the chief soil boundaries are generally associated with changes in slope and, once the relationships between land-form and soil have been recognized, the lines of traverse may be chosen accordingly. Changes in semi-natural vegetation may also afford guides to boundary location, but on flat or gently undulating, cultivated land reliance has usually to be placed on a pattern of regularly spaced auger borings in each field. This was necessary on the flat coastal tracts around Altcar, where the change from the soils on links sand to the complex of soils associated with the alluvium, and to organic soils occurs with little apparent variation in surface relief. Where the soil pattern is so complicated that delimitation of individual soil series is impracticable at the scale used, the areas concerned are mapped as *soil complexes*, characterized in terms of the constituent series and their proportionate extent.

When the survey of the area is complete a draft soil map is prepared at the scale of 1 : 25,000 (2½ in. to 1 mile) and reduced to 1 : 63,360 (1 in. to 1 mile) for publication. Not all the boundaries inserted on the field sheets can be reproduced at this scale, and normally only soil series and complexes are shown separately.

In order to characterize the soil series, types and phases, representative sites are selected and profile pits dug, generally to a depth of about 3 ft. At each site the location, slope (in degrees), aspect, altitude, land use and vegetation are recorded, and the profile is described in standard terms (see Appendix). The depth, thickness and clarity of recognizable horizons are first noted, and the colour, mechanical composition, stoniness, consistence, and structure of each horizon are recorded, together with the kind and distribution of organic matter, the presence and amount of calcium carbonate and secondary mineral deposits, and the distribution of soil fauna and roots. Finally, the parent material and drainage status of the soil may be deduced from a consideration of profile and site characteristics.

TYPES OF SOIL FORMATION

Horizon Nomenclature

To facilitate discussion and comparison of soils it is convenient to designate horizons by a letter notation, the same symbol being applied to analogous horizons in profiles of similar type. The notation adopted in this memoir is as follows:

Organic and organo-mineral surface horizons

L	Undecomposed litter.
F	Partially decomposed litter.
H	Well-decomposed humus layer, low in mineral matter.
A	Mixed, mineral-organic layer.
Ap	Ploughed layer of cultivated soils.
Ag	An A horizon with rusty mottling, subject to periodic waterlogging.

Sub-surface horizons

E	Eluvial horizons, depleted of clay and/or sesquioxides.
Ea	Bleached (ash-like) horizon in podzolized soils.
Eb	Brown (paler when dry), friable, weak-structured horizon depleted of clay (characteristic of *sols lessivés*).
B	Altered horizon distinguished by colour and/or structure, or by illuvial concentrations of the following materials denoted by suffixes:

    t   illuviated clay, characteristic of *sols lessivés*,
    h   illuviated humus, characteristic of podzols,
    fe illuviated iron, characteristic of podzols.

C	A horizon that is little altered, except by gleying, and is either like or unlike the material in which overlying horizons have developed (where two or more distinct depositional layers occur in the lower part of the profile, they are designated C1, C2, etc.).
Bca Cca } etc.	A horizon containing appreciable amounts of redeposited (secondary) calcium carbonate.
Bg Cg } etc.	Mottled (gleyed) horizons subject to waterlogging; where gleying is only weakly expressed the suffix (g) is used.
A/C B/C } etc.	Horizons of transitional or intermediate character.

Even when a considerable body of evidence is available, it may be difficult to apply a symbol notation to particular horizons and in doubtful cases alternative symbols are given.

Because of similarities in parent material or mode of soil formation, profiles characteristic of different soil series often have important features in common, and by selecting certain of them a limited number of profile types, or types of soil formation can be distinguished to serve as a basis for classification into higher categories. The soil series in this area can be placed in four major soil groups, *viz:* brown earths, gley soils, organic soils and podzolized soils which, with suitable subdivisions, are shown in Table 7; the relationship between soil series or complexes and the parent material is also included.

Brown Earths

The profile of brown earths consists essentially of A, B and C horizons; the crumbly, humose A horizon grading into a brown subsoil or B horizon that merges into the parent material. Calcium carbonate, if originally present, has been leached from the profile and the surface and sub-surface horizons are more or less acid in reaction. As a result of biological activity, organic matter is humified and so intimately mixed with the mineral matter as to form a dark-coloured clay-humus complex (*mull*) that masks the brown colours of the hydrated iron oxides in the surface layers. The soils are generally freely drained and the brown or reddish brown colours in the sub-surface horizon indicate aerobic weathering and the oxidized state of the iron compounds. The ratio of silica to sesquioxides of the clay fraction remains practically constant throughout the profile.

Some of the soils, however, are not so well drained and are referred to as *gleyed brown earths*. The colour of the corresponding well drained soil is dominant but some rusty mottling occurs on root channels and structure faces, which themselves may be grey but there is no horizon that is dominantly grey due to gleying.

Where weathering has produced appreciable amounts of fine clay, there is a tendency, especially marked where the soil dries out seasonally, for the clay (together with associated oxides) to migrate in suspension from higher horizons and to accumulate at lower levels as coatings on structure faces and in pores. Eventually brown or yellowish, weakly structured Eb horizons become differentiated from denser, finer-textured and more brightly coloured Bt horizons with blocky or prismatic structures. Such brown earths have been distinguished in France and other European countries as *sols lessivés* (Duchaufour, 1960) and in Britain as leached brown soils (Avery, 1956). The processes leading to the formation of *sols lessivés* apparently operate at moderate acidity (pH 6·0–5·0) and are not attended by appreciable decomposition of the clay fraction. The soils are frequently derived from calcareous sediments when, as a result of continuous leaching, the differentiation of the Eb and Bt horizons apparently follows complete decalcification and consequent desaturation of the absorbing complex.

In the survey area freely drained brown earths are restricted to the isolated deposits of glacial sand and gravel on which the Newport and Ellerbeck series are found and to the outcrops of Keuper and Bunter sandstone occupied by the Clive and Bridgnorth soils; all four series, however, only cover 180 acres.

Gleyed brown earths are more widespread; the Cottam and Salwick series occur on the till and the Astley Hall series is found where a thin cover of sand overlies till on moderate slopes; together these soils cover 2,900 acres. In the Salwick and Cottam series the clay content increases down the profile and effectively reduces the rate of percolation so that slight waterlogging occurs above the zone of maximum clay content. The presence of a perched water-table at the junction of the sand and underlying till in the Astley Hall series results in

TABLE 7
Major Soil Groups in relation to Parent Materials and Soil Mapping Units

Major Soil Group	Sub-group	Parent Material	Mapping Unit (Series and Complexes)*
Brown Earth		Coarse-grained, reddish Bunter Sandstone	Bridgnorth series
		Coarse-grained, yellow and/or brown Keuper sandstone	Clive series
		Fluvio-glacial sand	Newport series
		Fluvio-glacial gravel	Ellerbeck series
	Gleyed brown earth	Reddish brown, fine-textured slightly calcareous till	Cottam series
		Reddish brown, medium to fine-textured slightly calcareous till with sandy inclusions	Salwick series
		Shirdley Hill Sand overlying till	Astley Hall series
Podzolized Soil	Humus-iron podzol	Coarse-grained, yellow and/or brown Keuper sandstone or Shirdley Hill Sand overlying till	Crannymoor series
Gley Soil	Surface-water gley soil	Reddish brown, fine-textured slightly calcareous till	Salop series
		Medium to fine-textured slightly calcareous till with sandy inclusions	Clifton series
	Ground-water gley soil	Shirdley Hill Sand overlying till	Rufford series
		Downholland Silt	Downholland complex
		Active and recent estuarine alluvium (calcareous)	Hesketh complex
		Active and recent riverine alluvium	Douglas complex
		Recent riverine alluvium	Alt complex
		Recent blown sand	Formby series
	Humic gley soil	Reddish brown fine-textured slightly calcareous till	Oakland series
		Reddish brown medium to fine-textured slightly calcareous till with sandy inclusions	Lea series
	Gley podzol	Shirdley Hill Sand overlying till	Sollom complex
Organic Soil		Acid Basin Peat (Early Raised Moss stage)	Turbary Moor complex
		Acid to neutral Basin Peat (Low Moor stage)	Altcar complex
		Lacustrine organic mud	Martin Mere complex

* Complexes are included on the basis of the classification of the dominant soil.

some gleying but the slope is sufficient to permit lateral movement of water and consequently this feature is weakly developed.

B horizons in which the presence of illuviated clay is well marked are restricted to soils associated with the reddish brown, fine-textured and slightly calcareous till (Cottam series). South of the Ribble the till is covered by Shirdley Hill Sand on which marling was formerly a widespread practice and the evidence of clay illuviation is inconclusive so that the soils are classified as brown earths or gleyed brown earths.

Podzolized Soils

In general, podzolized soils are well drained and have an acid, organic A horizon overlying a bleached (ash-like) Ea horizon which in turn overlies Bh and/or Bfe horizons formed by the deposition of humus and iron removed from the upper layers. The soils normally occur on acid parent materials and biological activity is so low that litter from heath plants and trees accumulates on the surface and *mor* or raw humus layers develop.

Well developed podzols are rare in this district and only occupy 1000 acres. Soils of the Crannymoor series found on both Shirdley Hill Sand and Triassic sandstone have well developed Bh and Bfe horizons but the raw humus and bleached Ea horizons are often mixed by cultivation and incorporated to form humose Ap horizons which frequently rest directly on the Bh and Bfe horizons.

Soils presumably at an early stage of development occur on the Dune Sand under coniferous plantations. Thick accumulations of pine-needle litter with well developed F layers overlie very thin bleached Ea horizons but Bh and Bfe horizons cannot be discerned.

The humus-iron podzol is usually a freely drained soil with the water-table some distance below the surface. Where the water-table rises higher into the profile the lower layers develop morphological features characteristic of gley soils whilst the upper horizons retain those of a podzol. Such soils are termed *gley podzols*, and generally have an Ea, Bfe or Bh, Cg horizon sequence. In this district the B horizon is not indurated as in the humus-iron podzol.

The sub-group is represented by the Sollom series formed on the Shirdley Hill Sand. The underlying till sufficiently prevents percolation to cause gleying in the lower horizons of the profile. This series is the major component of the Sollom complex which occupies 8,600 acres, and is the second most extensive group of soils in this district.

Gley Soils

Gley is a Russian word referring to the dominantly grey-coloured horizon occurring in permanently waterlogged soils where anaerobic conditions prevail. The process by which the grey colours are formed has already been described. It is convenient to divide gley soils into ground-water gley soils and surface-water gley soils according to the conditions under which they have formed.

Ground-water gley soils are associated with the complete or partial seasonal saturation of the profile from below by regional ground-water or by a local accumulation of water held up by an impermeable stratum below the soil profile. *Surface-water gley soils* are the result of the relative impermeability of some part of the soil profile itself; water falls on the soil faster than it can percolate through and a seasonal or permanent zone of saturation occurs within the profile. It is evident that characteristics of both surface-water and ground-water gley soils can be observed particularly in fine-textured soils on flat, low-lying sites and it is often difficult to distinguish true ground-water without digging to great depths.

When soil drainage is such that the soil is practically permanently waterlogged at the surface, decomposition of plant residues is very slow and organic matter accumulates on the surface. Where such accumulations occur and do not exceed 15 in. thick, the soils are classified as *peaty gley soils*. Peaty gley soils can result from either surface-water or ground-water fluctuations or a combination of both. Under cultivation, the organic matter is partly decomposed and partly mixed with the underlying mineral material to form a well-humified organic-rich surface horizon. The resulting profiles are then better described as *humic gley soils*.

The only examples of surface-water gley soils in the district are the Clifton and Salop series which occupy 3,100 acres. The flat sites on which they occur have a negligible run-off and the parent material is such that water only moves through it very slowly. The horizons above and below the grey horizon of maximum gleying are mottled. When surface-water causes prolonged water-logging in the A horizons and an organic-rich surface soil develops humic gley soils of the Lea and Oaklands series are separated. They are the very poorly drained counterparts of the Clifton and Salop series, but are less extensive, and only occupy 1,000 acres.

As a regional ground-water table occurs everywhere below approximately 25 ft. O.D., ground-water gley soils are the most extensive group on the map, occupying about 14,200 acres. Soils of the Hesketh, Alt and Douglas complexes and of the Formby series belong to this sub-group, as do the soils that occur in the hollows or slacks of the Dune Sand. The fine-textured soils in these complexes are, however, modified by slight gleying due to surface-water. The Rufford series is a ground-water gley soil in which the local ground-water table occurs at the junction of sand and the underlying till on sites where lateral run-off is negligible. Where the junction is close to the surface the soil has characters of a surface-water gley soil. The Downholland complex, covering 2,500 acres, includes soils with peaty surface horizons formed as a result of a high regional ground-water table. The fine-textured members of the complex are modified by the effects of surface-water in the same way as the Hesketh, Alt and Douglas complexes.

Organic Soils

Soils of the organic group are distinguished from peaty or humic gley soils when the surface accumulation of organic matter exceeds 15 in. The group includes soils derived from peat and subdivisions are based on botanical composition and the stage of the peat formation reached. The Turbary Moor complex, Altcar complex and Martin Mere complex occur on Raised Moss, Fen-carr Peat and organic muds respectively. Organic soils are particularly widespread south of the Ribble and, occupying 13,800 acres, are almost as widespread as ground-water gley soils.

Dune sand, occurring along the coast-line both north and south of the Ribble, is so recently deposited that profile development on the dunes consists of little more than the incorporation of small amounts of organic matter in the surface layer. The soils can be regarded as pararendzinas or soils with only an A horizon that passes into calcareous, unconsolidated mineral deposits (Kubiena, 1953).

Dune Sand covers about 5,200 acres, and is shown separately in the legend on the map.

Table 8 shows the actual and proportionate extent of the soil mapping units for both maps.

TABLE 8

Acreage and Proportionate Extent of the Mapping Units

Soil Mapping Unit	Acreage (to nearest 100 acres)	Percentage of area surveyed
Altcar complex	8,800	16·7
Sollom complex	8,600	16·3
Formby series	6,400	12·2
Dune Sand	5,200	9·9
Turbary Moor complex	4,900	9·3
Hesketh complex	3,300	6·3
Alt complex	2,800	5·3
Clifton series	2,600	4·9
Downholland complex	2,500	4·7
Astley Hall series	1,800	3·4
Douglas complex	1,000	1·9
Salwick series	1,000	1·9
Crannymoor series	1,000	1·9
Lea series	900	1·7
Rufford series	700	1·3
Salop series	500	0·9
Oaklands series	100	0·2
Cottam series	100	0·2
Soils covering less than 100 acres*	300	0·5
Built-up areas	18,300	—

* The Martin Mere complex covers 90 acres, the Ellerbeck, Bridgnorth and Clive series each occupy 50 acres and the Newport series only occupies 30 acres.

TABLE 9

Areas occupied by the Soil Groups

Soil Group	Percentage
Ground-water gley soils	19·97
Organic soils	19·47
Gley podzols	12·19
Dune Sand	7·37
Surface-water gley soils	4·46
Gleyed brown earths	4·02
Ground-water humic gley soils	3·57
Surface-water humic gley soils	1·47
Humus-iron podzols	1·34
Brown earths	0·25

From Table 9 it can be deduced that slightly more than one quarter of the area covered by the two sheets is built over and of the remaining three quarters, gley soils occupy approximately 30 per cent. A further 16 per cent. is covered by gley podzols and gleyed brown earths; organic soils occupy about 20 per cent. In other words the soils of about 65 per cent. of the area have more or less marked

3

drainage problems and, except the gleyed brown earths, require artificial drainage. Forty per cent. of the area is affected by a regional ground-water table, *i.e.* the ground-water gley soils (excluding the Rufford series) and the organic soils. The widespread occurrence of this regional ground-water near the surface in an area of low relief necessitates regional drainage schemes involving the construction of extensive main drains with sluices and pumping stations.

The remaining 9 per cent. of the area is covered by the naturally freely drained brown earths, podzols and the Dune Sand. About one fifth of the area mapped as Dune Sand is naturally poorly drained with ground-water gley soils occupying the dune slacks.

CHAPTER III

Soils from Sands and Sandstones

About 24,000 acres of the area surveyed are covered by sandy soils nearly one-half of which are included in the Dune Sand and Formby series developed in recent blown sand. Approximately 11,000 acres are occupied by soils formed in sandy superficial deposits overlying clayey till. Brown earths of the Bridgnorth and Clive series, developed on Triassic sandstones, are of very small extent as are those of the Ellerbeck and Newport series found on fluvio-glacial gravel and sand. Some of the extensive area occupied by recent blown sand is forested but the greater part is of little agricultural importance although a small part is used for growing asparagus. Naturally well drained soils are not extensive for the sandy soils usually occur on low-lying land where the regional water-table is near the surface. The extensive Sollom complex comprises most of the latter area but where such soils are artificially drained, they are highly productive when adequately fertilized.

In addition to the Dune Sand, nine soil series and one complex have been distinguished; they are considered in the following order:

Soils from Triassic sandstones:
> Bridgnorth series,
> Clive series,
> Crannymoor series.

Soils from fluvio-glacial sand and gravel:
> Ellerbeck series,
> Newport series.

Soils from Shirdley Hill Sand:
> Astley Hall series,
> Rufford series,
> Sollom complex,
> Crannymoor series.

Soils from recent blown sand:
> Dune Sand,
> Formby series.

SOILS FROM TRIASSIC SANDSTONES

The cover of drift on the Lancashire plain is so extensive that there are few exposures of Bunter sandstone at the surface and subdivisions of the beds have not been shown on the Geological Survey map (Formby, 1942). The sandstone crops out around Walton and Bootle within the urban areas and only at Melling, where it forms an outstanding hillock, is there any development of a soil profile. Wray

27

and Cope (1948) state that the rocks are "coarse-grained, reddish, false-bedded sandstones with quartz pebbles, but also include bands of red and white free-stone".

Outcrops of Keuper sandstone are more widespread than those of the Bunter and occur as small isolated hillocks and ridges protruding through the till and Shirdley Hill Sand deposits. The sandstone is well developed around Ince Blundell, Thornton and Crosby where its colour varies from light grey to yellow and brown. At Lydiate it is bright yellow and, at Hillhouse, a massive, yellow, coarse-grained sandstone is exposed. The sandstone outcrop forms the low Clieves Hills which attain a maximum of 175 ft. O.D. in the area under consideration.

BRIDGNORTH SERIES

The soils of this series, first described in Shropshire (Crompton and Osmond, 1954), are formed in the false-bedded, reddish brown Bunter sandstone which occurs only on the Formby sheet around Melling. They occupy 50 acres on a low ridge with elevations from 60 to 100 ft. and are developed under conditions of free drainage that arise from the combination of a permeable rock and a well drained site. The depth of soil over the weathering sandstone is variable but rarely exceeds 30 in. and then only on the lower gentler slopes; where rock appears at less than 12 in., generally on upper slopes, the soil is regarded as a shallow phase of the series. Soil profiles are freely drained, or even excessively drained where the shallow phase occurs, and show little differentiation between horizons. Colours are reasonably uniform throughout, although the cultivation layer is darker as a result of the incorporation of organic matter.

Under grass, the A horizon is a friable to very friable, dark brown, coarse sandy loam or loamy coarse sand with weakly developed sub-angular blocky structures. The organic-matter content is generally moderate under permanent grassland but tends to be low under arable cropping and the humus form is mull. A sharp change takes place at plough depth into the B horizon of reddish brown, sandy loam, with a very weakly developed blocky structure and low organic-matter content, which merges into structureless sand with an increasing number of weathering sandstone fragments. This overlies the slightly weathered hard red sandstone.

Structures in the profile are only weakly developed because of the small percentage of clay and, furthermore, the low exchange capacity is closely related to the combination of low contents of clay and organic matter. There are indications that the soil has been marled (p. 98) in the past, but this has not substantially increased the clay content of the surface horizons. Moderate to low pH values indicate the need for regular and frequent liming, and the leaching of calcium and magnesium through the profile is indicated by both the increase in the amount of these bases in the exchangeable form and by the base saturation of the B2 horizon compared with that of the A horizon.

Description of a representative profile

PROFILE NO.: La 120, Bridgnorth series; (analysis, p. 87).
Location: Melling (grid ref. SD 389001).
Relief: near crest of sandstone ridge.
Slope: 1°. *Aspect:* south. *Altitude:* 96 ft. O.D.
Parent Material: Bunter sandstone.

Land Use: permanent grassland.
Horizons:

in.

0–9
A
Dark brown (7·5 YR 3/2) coarse sandy loam with occasional small rounded stones of various origins and sandstone fragments; weak medium sub-angular blocky and granular structures; abundant pores; friable; moderate organic-matter content and abundant fine fibrous roots; occasional earth-worms; cinders present; non-calcareous; sharp, even boundary.

9–16
B1
Reddish brown (5 YR 4/3) coarse sandy loam with occasional sandstone fragments; very weak medium blocky structure; abundant pores; very friable; low organic-matter content, fine fibrous roots common; few earth-worm channels; non-calcareous; merging, even boundary.

16–27
B2
Reddish brown (5 YR 4/4) sandy loam with occasional sandstone frag-ments; structureless; loose; abundant pores; low organic-matter content; few fine fibrous roots; non-calcareous; sharp, undulating boundary.

27+
C
Slightly weathered red sandstone with pinkish red and grey horizontal bands.

CLIVE SERIES

This series which was first mapped in Shropshire (Crompton and Osmond, 1954), occupies 50 acres on the Formby sheet. It represents the freely drained brown earth developed on Keuper sandstone. The soils occupy both gentle and steep slopes and profile drainage is generally free although the shallow phase, found where rock occurs at less than 12 in., is excessively drained. The soils are very similar to those of the Bridgnorth series and mechanical and chemical analyses confirm the close resemblance.

Under grassland the A horizon is dark brown or dark greyish brown, typically of sandy loam texture, but occasionally loamy sand, with weakly developed sub-angular blocky and granular or crumb structures. The organic-matter content is generally moderate but under continuous arable cropping it can become extremely low. There is a fairly sharp boundary to the A horizon, generally at cultivation depth, beneath which the B horizon is a yellowish brown or brown, sandy loam with very weakly developed sub-angular blocky structures. Weather-ing sandstone fragments become dominant towards the base of the horizon which may be structureless and sandy. The C horizon, which normally occurs at about 2 ft., consists of horizontally-bedded weathering sandstone with the interstices filled with sandy loam and with faint humus staining along fissures.

Structures are very weakly developed throughout the profile owing to the low content of clay and organic matter. Although drainage is generally free, some profiles under permanent pasture have faint rusty mottles along old root channels in the surface layer which may be due to slight impedence to water movement resulting from the destruction of the weak structures by treading by stock and subsequent compaction of the surface. The shallow phase on the steeper slopes may be excessively drained and subject to drought owing to run-off and the high permeability of the profile. Unless adequate dressings of lime and fertilizers are given the surface horizons are acid and the content of exchangeable bases is low. That these properties can be greatly modified by management is shown by the analytical data for profile La 129 under permanent grassland in which the exchange capacity of the surface is saturated and that of the B horizon is 79 per cent. saturated and the reaction is near neutral.

Description of a representative profile

PROFILE NO.: La 129, Clive series; (analysis, p. 87).
Location: Ince Blundell Park (grid ref. SD 332027).
Relief: crest of sandstone ridge.
Slope: 1°. *Aspect:* east. *Altitude:* 50 ft. O.D.
Parent Material: Keuper sandstone.
Land Use: permanent grassland.
Horizons:

in.		
0–8 A	Dark greyish brown (10 YR 4/2) coarse sandy loam with bleached sand grains and faint rusty mottling on old root channels; stoneless; medium sub-angular blocky and granular structures; abundant pores; friable; moderate organic-matter content, abundant fine roots; earthworms common; occasional cinders indicative of night-soiling; non-calcareous; sharp, even boundary.
8–21 B	Dark yellowish brown (10 YR 4/4) sandy loam with occasional sandstone fragments; very weak medium sub-angular blocky structure; abundant pores; very friable; low organic-matter content, fine roots common; few earthworms; non-calcareous; merging, even boundary.
21+ C	Strong brown (7·5 YR 5/8) horizontally-bedded sandstone with some humus staining along fissures.

CRANNYMOOR SERIES

The series as named and mapped in Shropshire (Crompton and Osmond, 1954) is regarded as a humus-iron podzol formed on Bunter sandstone or glacial sand and gravel derived mainly from Triassic sandstones. The field morphology of humus-iron podzols developed on Keuper sandstone is so similar that they are included in the series although in the surveyed area the soils are shallow and rock frequently occurs close to the surface. The 480 acres of this soil represent the dominant series formed on Keuper sandstone on the Formby sheet. Most of the soils, even though shallow, have been cultivated so that profiles with the characteristic bleached Ea horizon are now rarely found. The very dark brown or black A horizon of sandy loam or loamy sand contains many bleached sand grains derived from the former Ea horizon and has a high organic-matter content; the soft crumb or granular structures are weakly developed. The surface layers merge into a dark reddish brown Bhfe horizon of sand or sandy loam texture, parts of which are weakly cemented with humus and iron compounds, and where many small ferruginous concretions occur. The brownish yellow sandstone rock, which occurs usually at a depth of between 6 and 12 in. lies immediately beneath this horizon.

Where management is poor or the soils are uncultivated the profile is moderately acid throughout with pH values of 5·0 to 5·5 in the surface horizon increasing to about 6·0 in the lowest horizons. The content of exchangeable bases is low and decreases with depth. Under cultivation, the surface soils are often maintained near neutrality and improvement in soil reaction, percentage saturation, and content of exchangeable bases is brought about by regular applications of lime and fertilizers.

Description of a representative profile

PROFILE NO.: La 90, Crannymoor series, rocky phase; (analysis, p. 88).
Location: Clieves Hills (grid ref. SD 384081).
Relief: side of sandstone ridge.

Slope: 2°. *Aspect:* south. *Altitude:* 165 ft. O.D.
Parent Material: Keuper sandstone.
Land Use: permanent grassland.
Horizons:

.in.	
0–2	Very dark brown (10 YR 2/2) loamy sand with bleached sand grains; few
A1	weathering sandstone fragments; weak granular structure; very friable; high organic-matter content; abundant fine roots; earthworms present; recently limed, cinders present; non-calcareous; merging, even boundary.
2–9	Very dark greyish brown (10 YR 3/2) loamy sand with yellow sand grains;
A2	occasional large fragments of yellowish brown sandstone; weak sub-angular blocky and granular structures; abundant pores; very friable; high organic-matter content, abundant fibrous roots; earthworms present; non-calcareous; merging, even boundary.
9–10	Dark reddish brown (5 YR 3/2) sandy loam with many orange-coloured
Bhfe	mottles, humus stains and small iron concretions; few sandstone fragments; structureless; loose; high organic-matter content mainly confined to root and earthworm channels; non-calcareous; merging, irregular boundary.
10–12	Brownish yellow (10 YR 6/6) sand with dark greyish brown horizontal
B/C	bands; abundant fragments of sandstone; structureless; loose; abundant pores and large fissures; low organic-matter content, few fine roots mainly confined to fissures; iron staining on the sandstone; non-calcareous; merging, even boundary.
12+	Strong brown (7·5 YR 5/8) coarse-grained horizontally-bedded sandstone
C	with some dark brown staining in horizontal and vertical fissures.

The soils of the Clive and Crannymoor series formed on Keuper sandstone and of the Bridgnorth series on Bunter sandstone are suited to arable cultivation and their use therefore conforms to the general farming pattern on the Formby sheet. They are easy to cultivate because of their sandy texture and freely draining nature. The principal crops are oats, barley, brassicas and potatoes with short-term leys included in the rotation to increase the content of organic matter and to maintain soil structure. Where rock is near the surface and the slope is such that cultivation is difficult, the soils are invariably under permanent pasture which, however, is subject to drought in dry periods.

Because the clay content is low, the cation-exchange capacity of the surface soil is closely related to the amount of organic matter. The natural fertility of the soils is low and they are generally low in potash and frequent applications of fertilizer and the maintenance of pH values at about 6·0 to 6·5 by repeated small applications of lime are necessary for optimum growth of crops. The liberal use of organic manures to increase the water-retaining capacity is extremely beneficial to these soils which have a low moisture-holding capacity and consequently suffer from drought during long dry periods.

It is probable that the natural vegetation on the Triassic sandstones was either oak-birch heath or mixed high forest. No remnants of the heath community remain but a stand of semi-natural mixed high forest on Keuper sandstone was examined at Ince Blundell (grid ref. SD 332027). The stand is situated on the Clive series and the humus form is moder with well developed F and H layers. The tree stratum of the woodland consists of sycamore (*Acer pseudoplatanus*), elm (*Ulmus procera*), oak (*Quercus robur*), beech (*Fagus sylvatica*), lime (*Tilia vulgaris*), and sweet chestnut (*Castanea sativa*) with an average density of 24 stems per acre and breast-height diameter ranging from 16 to 34 in., maximum height of stand 70 ft., canopy height 35 ft. and canopy density 75 per cent. There is a well developed understorey of naturally regenerated sycamore consisting of occasional trees in the low pole stage, average height 40 ft., average breast-height diameter 6 in., and with dense patches at the thicket stage. Elder (*Sambucus nigra*) and holly (*Ilex aquifolium*) occur sporadically. Much of the ground is bare of vegetation especially beneath dense regenerating sycamore and the low canopy of some of the older trees. Where present, the ground-flora is a sparse cover of Yorkshire fog (*Holcus lanatus*), common bent (*Agrostis tenuis*), bramble (*Rubus* spp.), stinging nettle (*Urtica dioica*), sheep's fescue (*Festuca ovina*) and patches of the moss *Mnium hornum*.

SOILS FROM FLUVIO-GLACIAL SAND AND GRAVEL

Deposits of glacial sand and gravel occur sporadically in the form of ridges and mounds. North of the Ribble, deposits of coarse gravel are rare but sandy deposits are more common notably in the Westby with Plumptons district. Two soil series have been identified: the Newport series formed both on fine and coarse sand and the Ellerbeck series on a mixture of sand and gravel. Both are brown earths that are freely drained although in the shallow phases the presence of the underlying till may cause percolating water to be held in the substrata and cause slight gleying in the lower parts of the profile.

ELLERBECK SERIES

This series occupies only 10 acres on the Southport sheet and 40 acres on the Formby sheet. The soil was first named and described near Preston (Crompton, 1966) and occurs in small patches, usually where there are marked ridges and hillocks with moderate to gentle slopes so that water runs off the site. The profile drainage is generally free.

The diagnostic features of the soils of the Ellerbeck series are the gravelly and sandy loam texture, the abundance of rounded stones and pebbles, a dark brown or brown A horizon, free drainage and profiles with little differentiation into horizons.

Typical profiles have a dark brown or brown A horizon 6–11 in. thick of gravelly loam or sandy loam with weak sub-angular blocky and granular structures; the organic-matter content is generally moderate. This passes sharply at plough depth to a brighter-coloured, sandy loam B horizon with abundant rounded stones of various sizes, up to 6 in. in their longer diameter. The stones are of varied origin and include hard Lakeland rocks with some Carboniferous sandstones. The C horizon is dominated by stones between which is a matrix of yellowish red or brown sandy loam. Although there is little variation in texture down the profile the proportions of stones and gravel vary considerably. Some fine ochreous mottling and faint manganiferous staining may occur in the lower horizons.

Moderate amounts of organic matter are well distributed throughout the surface horizon, especially under permanent grassland, but a low clay content is responsible for only a moderate base-exchange capacity and weakly developed structures. Rainwater percolates rapidly and the surface soil is normally slightly to moderately acid, with pH values of 5·5 to 6·0 so that regular liming is essential for the optimum growth of most crops.

Description of a representative profile

PROFILE NO.: La 106, Ellerbeck series; (analysis, p. 89).
Location: Aughton (grid ref. SD 381052).
Relief: minor ridge in gently undulating plain.
Slope: 1°. *Aspect:* west. *Altitude:* 60 ft. O.D.
Parent Material: glacial sand and gravel.
Land Use: ley grassland.
Horizons:

in.

0–11 Ap	Dark brown (7·5 YR 3/2) very stony sandy loam; gravel and rounded small and medium stones of mixed origin; weakly developed fine to medium, sub-angular blocky and granular structures; friable; high organic-matter content, abundant fine roots; numerous earthworms; recently limed; merging, even boundary.
11–15 B1	Brown (7·5 YR 4/4) very stony sandy loam; weakly developed fine to medium sub-angular blocky structures; very friable; moderate amount of organic matter, fine roots common; occasional earthworms; merging, irregular boundary.
15–20 B2	Yellowish red (5 YR 5/6) very stony loamy sand; very weakly developed fine angular blocky structure; very friable; moderate organic-matter content, few fine roots; occasional earthworms; occasional small black manganiferous concretions; merging, irregular boundary.
20–27 C1	Brown (7·5 YR 5/4) sandy loam, becoming greyer towards base of horizon; extremely stony with gravel and rounded small and medium stones; structureless; loose; very porous; moderate organic-matter content; few small black manganiferous concretions and coatings on gravel; merging, irregular boundary.
27+ C2	Reddish brown (5 YR 4/3) stony clay loam with prominent grey (5 YR 5/1) mottles on structure faces; strongly developed coarse prismatic structure; firm; moderate organic-matter content, roots very rare; abundant small black manganiferous concretions.

NEWPORT SERIES

This series, which only covers 30 acres on the Southport sheet, was originally described and mapped in the Vale of Clwyd (Hughes and Walters, 1932) and was more fully described later in Shropshire (Crompton and Osmond, 1954). It is a freely drained brown earth formed on glacial sand with a variable, but small proportion of gravel and pebbles, the sand usually being reddish brown or yellowish brown in colour. The soils are confined to small ridges and hillocks on the undulating ground near Westby and Little Plumpton where slopes are gentle to moderate. On the steeper slopes run-off is considerable; profile drainage is invariably free and may be excessive on the more pronounced gradients.

Typical profiles have an A horizon of very dark greyish brown or brown, friable, loamy sand or sandy loam, 6–9 in. thick, with moderately developed sub-angular blocky and granular structures. The organic-matter content is generally moderate under old grassland but is invariably low under arable cropping and decreases rapidly down the profile. The A horizon merges into the B horizon which is dark brown or brown, loamy sand or sandy loam with weaker and less developed structures. The C horizon consists of brown or yellowish brown loose sand. There is every possibility that these soils have been marled in the past and the somewhat higher clay content of the surface may be due to this addition of finer material. The cation-exchange capacity is generally low and decreases with depth, being closely related to the low content of clay and organic matter in the solum. The content of exchangeable calcium in the surface horizon is moderate, averaging about 6·0 to 7·0 m.e. per 100 g. of soil but is very low in the C horizon. The higher content of exchangeable calcium and other bases in the surface in many cases results from the frequent addition of lime and fertilizers, for the series is inherently poor in plant nutrients and bases and is acid in reaction with pH values of 5·0 to 5·5. These soils, therefore, require regular applications of lime and fertilizers for optimum growth of most crops.

Description of a representative profile

PROFILE NO.: La 122, Newport series; (analysis, p. 91).
Location: Warton (grid ref. SD 389287).
Relief: minor ridge in gently undulating plain.
Slope: 2°. *Aspect:* west. *Altitude:* 25 ft. O.D.
Parent Material: glacial sand and gravel.
Land Use: permanent grassland.
Horizons:

in.		
0–9	Dark greyish brown (10 YR 4/2) sandy loam; occasional small rounded
A	stones; moderately developed fine to medium sub-angular blocky and granular structures; friable; abundant fine and medium pores; moderate amount of organic matter, abundant fine and small fibrous roots; numerous earthworms; narrow, even boundary.
9–15	Dark brown (7·5 YR 4/2) slightly stony loamy sand; very weakly devel-
B	oped sub-angular blocky structure; very friable; very porous; low organic-matter content, fine and small fibrous roots common; occasional earthworms; merging, irregular boundary.
15+	Brown (7·5 YR 5/4) stoneless sand; structureless; loose; fine and medium
C	pores extremely abundant; very low organic-matter content.

The soils of the Ellerbeck and Newport series are generally distributed as small patches and, consequently, are managed according to the farming pattern of the area of their occurrence. North of the Ribble, therefore, the soils are generally under permanent grass but south of the river they are mainly in arable. The soils are well suited to arable crops because their coarse texture and free drainage contribute to ease of working under most weather conditions. Their low moisture-holding capacity renders crops, particularly permanent grass, liable to suffer from drought. Frequent and heavy applications of organic manures help to overcome this defect. Although the inherent nutrient status is low and the rapid leaching leads to further loss good crops can be produced if adequate dressings of lime and fertilizers are given.

The deposits have been used as a source of sand and gravel and a few disused pits are to be found.

SOILS FROM SHIRDLEY HILL SAND

A post-glacial deposit of sand, covering large areas south of the Ribble, stretches from Scarisbrick to Aintree and also occurs around Ince Blundell. The original description (De Rance, 1870) was made at Shirdley Hill, 5 miles north-east of Formby. The deposit consists mainly of coarse sand, the grains of which are well rounded, and the frequent occurrence of cross-bedding indicates its sub-aerial and wind-blown mode of deposition. The deposit overlies till or, less frequently, Triassic rocks, and it is generally between 1 and 3 ft. thick although thicknesses of up to 15 ft. have been recorded in borings at Haskayne and Little Crosby.

The relief of the whole area of deposition is gently undulating at elevations between 25 and 75 ft. O.D. The veneer of sand has tended to fill depressions in the former landscape developed in the till so that although the present land surface appears to be fairly level, the thickness of the sand varies rapidly and erratically. Furthermore, the till frequently protrudes through the sand forming marked hillocks and ridges on which soils of the Salwick and Clifton series are found. On the western slopes of Clieves Hills the sand occasionally reaches heights in excess of 150 ft. O.D.

Although features associated with sand dunes are rare, small elongated mounds, west of Haskayne and trending W.N.W.–E.S.E. probably represent relic dunes of the Hillhouse Coastline.

The profiles of the four soil series (Astley Hall, Rufford, Sollom and Crannymoor) distinguished on the Shirdley Hill Sand are differentiated by their natural drainage characteristics which differ according to the degree of slope and the thickness of sand overlying till. Although the sand itself is readily permeable the till forms a relatively impermeable barrier to the downward movement of water through the profile and water held at the junction of the sand and till produces features of drainage impedence in the subsoil. A complete hydrologic sequence has not been recognized, however, as no freely drained member has been recorded.

The Astley Hall series occurs on sites from which there is considerable run-off. These imperfectly drained soils have variable amounts of grey and rust mottling at the junction of the sand and till and are grouped with the gleyed brown earths. The Rufford series is confined to more gentle slopes and flat areas where the degree of gleying is much more intense and the soils are included in the gley soils. The Crannymoor series, a humus-iron podzol, occurs sporadically on slightly elevated positions as well as on flat sites. The gley podzols of the Sollom series are not separately delimited but are part of the 8,600 acres of the Sollom complex that also includes humic gley soils and podzols of the Crannymoor series.

Considerable areas of Shirdley Hill Sand have been marled with material dug from the underlying reddish brown till. This not only supplied calcium carbonate to reduce the acidity but also added other minerals and, by increasing the clay content in the surface horizon, reduced the liability to dessication and blowing during dry periods. It has not been possible to determine accurately the rates and frequency of application of marl but amounts up to 200 tons per acre may have been used. In profile examinations an increased clay content of the surface horizon and the presence of rounded and sub-angular stones indicate where marling has taken place.

ASTLEY HALL SERIES

The Astley Hall series comprises imperfectly drained loamy sands and sandy loams formed on Shirdley Hill Sand resting on reddish brown till that occurs at depths ranging from 12 in. to 3 ft. or more. It covers 1,730 acres on the Formby sheet but only 40 acres south of the Ribble on the Southport sheet.

The soils occur mostly on upper parts of ridges where the steepest slopes rarely exceed 3°. They often merge down-hill into soils of the Rufford series and up-slope may pass into soils of the Salwick and Cottam series where the till crops out at the surface.

The presence of the less permeable underlying till impedes the vertical downward movement of water from the coarser-textured upper layers and the water tends to move laterally down-slope within the profile and to produce grey and ochreous mottling in the subsoil characteristic of imperfectly drained soils.

The A horizon consists of brown to dark brown, loamy sand to sandy loam with faint rusty mottling along root channels. It usually has weakly developed sub-angular blocky and granular structures at the surface passing at 8–10 in. into a B horizon of brown loamy sand with very weakly developed medium angular blocky structures. This merges into brown loamy sand or sand, designated B(g), with faint orange-brown and grey mottling on structural faces and also within the peds. The structures are very weakly developed medium angular blocky and in some profiles the horizon may be structureless. The reddish brown till of clay loam to silty clay texture with distinct orange-brown and grey mottling on structure faces is usually encountered between 12 and 36 in. The soils are of low base status with pH values typically ranging from 5·5 to 6·0 in the A horizon and increasing to 6·5 to 7·0 in the Cg horizon which is generally base saturated.

These comparatively easy-working soils are well suited to arable cultivation. Artificial drainage may be necessary for maximum production and crops respond satisfactorily to regular applications of lime and fertilizers.

Description of a representative profile

PROFILE NO.: La 103, Astley Hall series; (analysis, p. 86).
Location: Little Crosby (grid ref. SD 320011).
Relief: gentle slope in undulating plain.
Slope: 1°. *Aspect:* north-west. *Altitude:* 50 ft. O.D.
Parent Material: Shirdley Hill Sand overlying fine-textured till.
Land Use: ley grassland.
Horizons:

in.

0–10
Ap
Dark brown (7·5 YR 4/2) loamy sand with faint reddish brown mottles along root channels and frequent bleached sand grains; occasional small rounded stones and cinders; weakly developed medium sub-angular blocky and granular structures; firm; moderate organic-matter content, small roots abundant; frequent earthworms; sharp, even boundary.

10–22
B
Brown (7·5 YR 5/4) loamy sand; few small rounded stones; very weakly developed medium angular blocky structure; friable; low organic-matter content, small roots common; merging, even boundary.

22–28
B(g)
Brown (7·5 YR 5/2) loamy sand with faint orange-brown and grey mottles and grey structure faces; very weakly developed medium angular blocky structure; low organic-matter content, very few fine roots; sharp, even boundary.

28+
Cg
Reddish brown (5 YR 4/3) clay loam with distinct orange-brown and grey mottles and dark grey (5 Y 4/1) on structure faces; small rounded stones; moderately developed coarse prismatic structure; firm; moderate organic-matter content; occasional small soft black manganiferous concretions.

RUFFORD SERIES

The Rufford series, covering 685 acres on the Formby sheet, is formed, like the Astley Hall series, in Shirdley Hill Sand overlying relatively impermeable till. The Astley Hall series passes downslope into the Rufford series which is commonly found on 1° and 2° slopes. On such nearly level sites the lateral flow of water is considerably reduced, the effects of the impedence of drainage at the junction of the sand and till are therefore more marked and the B horizon, which in the Astley Hall series is brown with faint rusty mottles, has a pronounced light brownish grey or drab grey colour with distinct brown mottles and is often lacking structural units, features that are typical of gleyed horizons in coarse-textured deposits.

The transition from the Astley Hall series is gradual and the surface horizon of the Rufford series is very dark greyish brown in colour compared with the dark brown colour of the Astley Hall soils. Distinct brown staining and mottles are associated with old roots and the texture ranges from loamy sand to sandy loam with weakly to moderately developed sub-angular blocky and granular structures. The surface horizon merges into a Bg horizon of light brownish grey, rust mottled, loamy sand or sand which is normally loose and structureless and overlies the reddish brown till.

The transition zone (Bg/Cg) between sand and till is often marked by a strong brown, sandy clay loam or clay loam horizon with distinct grey mottles and coatings on prismatic structure faces and many small manganiferous concretions. The thickness of the sand is very variable ranging generally from 1 to 3 ft. although in some places the presence of till can only be inferred from the increasing wetness and the grey colours in the sand at about 3 ft.

The content of organic matter is moderate to low in the A(g) horizon and decreases rapidly in the Bg horizon so that there is a marked colour change at this level. Weakly developed structures in the surface horizon are a result of low contents of organic matter and clay. The cation-exchange capacity is low and the percentage saturation and pH values are comparable with those of the Astley Hall profile quoted.

Waterlogging seems to be particularly serious in soils of the Rufford series but where an adequate drainage system is maintained the soils are well suited to arable cultivation for the surface soils are easy to work and the presence of the less pervious underlying till assures that there is a reserve of moisture during dry periods.

Description of a representative profile

PROFILE NO.: La 104, Rufford series; (analysis, p. 91).
Location: Little Crosby (grid ref. SD 318008).
Relief: base of gentle slope in undulating plain.
Altitude: 40 ft. O.D.
Parent Material: Shirdley Hill Sand overlying fine-textured till.
Land Use: ley grassland.
Horizons:

in.

0–9
Ap(g)
Very dark greyish brown (10 YR 3/2) sandy loam with distinct fine reddish brown mottles along root channels; occasional small rounded stones of varied origins; friable; weakly developed fine sub-angular blocky and granular structures; moderate organic-matter content, abundant fine roots; occasional earthworms; merging, undulating boundary.

9–13   Light brownish grey (10 YR 6/2) loamy sand with prominent brown
Bg   mottles (10 YR 5/3); stoneless; structureless; loose; very low organic-
        matter content, fine roots rare; sharp, irregular boundary.
13–17   Strong brown (7·5 YR 5/8) clay loam with many prominent grey (10 YR 6/1)
Bg/Cg   mottles, most pronounced on structure faces; occasional small rounded
        stones of varied origins; moderately developed coarse prismatic struc-
        tures; moderate organic-matter content; plastic; small soft mangani-
        ferous concretions common; sharp, irregular boundary.
17+   Reddish brown (5 YR 4/3) slightly stony clay loam with prominent dark
Cg   grey (5 YR 4/1) mottles on structure faces; strongly developed coarse
        prismatic structure; plastic; moderate organic-matter content; few small
        soft manganiferous concretions.

SOLLOM COMPLEX

Four hundred acres on the Southport sheet and 8,200 acres on the Formby
sheet are shown as the Sollom complex on flat or very gently undulating land
with slopes of less than 1 degree. The main constituent is the Sollom series;
while podzols of the Crannymoor series and humic gley soils occupy smaller
areas.

This diversity of soil profiles within short distances may be attributed to the
interaction of a variable ground-water table with varying thicknesses of sand over
till. Where the sand is sufficiently thick and the ground-water is well below the
surface, podzols of the Crannymoor series can develop; they can also form on
slight elevations. At the other extreme, the ground-water can be (or has been)
sufficiently close to the surface for peat to develop and even to extend over
adjacent higher land. Large areas appear to have been covered by peat but the
substantial lowering of the water-table by artificial drainage followed by wastage
and the mixing of the surface layers by cultivation has led to its disappearance
though, even today, some surface soils are distinctly peaty particularly in
depressions or adjacent to the remaining areas of peat. Elsewhere, because of the
thinness of the sand overlying the till, the ground-water has remained nearer
to the surface and the horizon sequence Ea, Bh and/or Bfe, C characteristic of
podzols has been modified or curtailed. Profiles with A, C; A, Ea, C; A, Ea, Bh
and/or Bfe horizon sequences accompanied by gleying can, therefore, occur
though usually in such a complex distribution as to be impracticable to map
separately at the scale used.

The major component of the complex, the Sollom series, is confined almost
entirely to sites with slopes of less than 1 degree. The soils are included in the
group of gley podzols, the identifying features being peaty or humose, sandy
surface soils overlying almost white, structureless sand with a weakly developed
slightly coherent humus or iron B horizon (*Plate V b*).

The A horizon is a friable, very dark brown or black sand, loamy sand or
sandy loam containing many bleached sand grains and having weakly developed
sub-angular blocky and granular or soft crumb structures. There is a sharp
boundary, generally at cultivation depth, at the Ea horizon which consists of
light brownish grey or pale grey structureless, loose sand. In some instances the
sand is almost pure white but it usually becomes humus-stained lower in the
profile although it remains loose or very friable when moist and is only slightly
hard when dry. Typically it merges into a brown or dark brown Bh or Bfe
horizon of structureless sand where sesquioxides or humus have accumulated.

This horizon is neither cemented nor indurated as it is in the profile of the Crannymoor series. A sharp change to reddish brown till commonly occurs between 2 and 4 ft.

Where the cover of sand is thin and the clay till occurs within 2 ft. of the surface, a shallow phase is recognized (profile La 114). The Ap horizon is typically black humose loamy sand and overlies very dark grey structureless sand with many black stained grains and many large distinct black mottles. This passes sharply to a thin transition horizon of greyish brown, sandy clay loam with prominent grey and brown mottles associated with structure faces and old root channels. Beneath this is reddish brown, clay loam with strongly developed prismatic structures.

The analytical data clearly illustrate the high organic-matter content of the A horizon and the sharp fall in the Ea horizon. The effect of this on the cation-exchange capacity, which decreases from 27 m.e./100 g. in the A horizon to 1 m.e./100 g. in the Ea horizon, is strikingly demonstrated. Cation-exchange capacity in the A horizon is approximately 3 times higher in the Sollom series than in the Astley Hall and Rufford series in which the contents of organic matter are very much lower. The percentage saturation, however, is generally low in the surface horizons and pH values between 4·5 and 5·5 are associated with the peaty and humose surfaces.

The soils of the Sollom series are very widely cultivated in south-west Lancashire. The inherent fertility is very low and production of crops is dependent almost entirely on added manures, but the peaty or humose character of the surface layers confers a good moisture-holding and high cation-exchange capacity. The ease of working under most weather conditions makes the soils ideal for intensive arable cultivation where an adequate drainage system has been installed.

Of common occurrence but limited extent at the edge of the mosslands, between the Sollom soils and those of the Altcar or Turbary Moor complex, is a soil from which almost all the former cover of peat has been lost and into the surface of which more recent blown sand has been mixed by cultivation (profile La 112). The cultivated profile generally shows about 10 in. of black peaty sand or loamy sand overlying 2 to 4 in. of black or very dark brown amorphous peat. This passes sharply into very dark grey peaty sand, 2–3 in. thick, that overlies very pale brownish grey sand of variable thickness. The till is generally within 3 ft. of the surface.

Profiles from which the B horizon is absent and, therefore, consist of a dark-coloured A horizon passing directly into a bleached Cg horizon are included in the complex and although found farther east (Crompton, 1966) are very in-frequent in the Southport and Formby areas.

Descriptions of representative profiles

PROFILE NO.: La 88, Sollom series; (analysis, p. 92).
Location: Downholland Cross (grid ref. SD 353068).
Relief: even slope in gently undulating plain.
Slope: 1°. *Aspect:* west. *Altitude:* 20 ft. O.D.
Parent Material: Shirdley Hill Sand overlying fine-textured till.
Land Use: ley grassland.
Horizons:

in.

0–8   Black (10 YR 2/0) humose sand with many bleached sand grains; weakly

Ap	developed medium crumb structure; friable; abundant small fibrous roots; occasional earthworms; sharp, even boundary.
8–14 Ea	Light brownish grey (10 YR 6/2) sand with few faint black mottles; stoneless; structureless; loose; very low organic-matter content, few fine roots; merging, irregular boundary.
14–24 Bfe	Dark brown (7·5 YR 4/2) sand with many distinct black mottles; stoneless; structureless; loose; very low organic matter, roots rare, mainly dead; merging, irregular boundary.
24–33 B/Cg	Pale brown (10 YR 6/3) sand with few faint strong brown (7·5 YR 5/6) mottles; stoneless; structureless; loose; very low organic-matter content; dead roots very rare; water-table standing at 33 in. on 24.2.59.

PROFILE NO.: La 114, Sollom series, shallow phase; (analysis, p. 92).
Location: Pinfold, nr. Scarisbrick (grid ref. SD 388111).
Relief: foot of slope in gently undulating plain.
Slope: 1°. *Aspect:* south-west. *Altitude:* 58 ft. O.D.
Parent Material: Shirdley Hill Sand overlying fine-textured till.
Land Use: ley grassland.
Horizons:
    in.

0–8 Ap	Black (10 YR 2/1) sandy loam with many bleached sand grains; weakly developed medium sub-angular blocky and granular structure; friable; abundant small fibrous roots; occasional earthworms; merging, even boundary.
8–13 Ea1	Black (10 YR 2/1) loamy sand with many distinct very dark grey (10 YR 3/1) mottles; stoneless; structureless; loose; few fine fibrous roots; occasional earthworms; merging, irregular boundary.
13–18 Ea2	Black (5 YR 2/1) sand; very weakly developed angular blocky structure; stoneless; few fine fibrous roots; occasional earthworms; sharp, even boundary.
18–20 B/Cg	Greyish brown (10 YR 5/2) sandy clay loam; occasional small and medium stones; weakly developed fine angular blocky structure; few fine fibrous roots; occasional earthworms; sharp, even boundary.
20–25 C(g)1	Strong brown (7·5 YR 5/6) clay with many distinct greyish brown (2·5 Y 5/2) mottles associated with structure faces and old root channels; occasional small and medium stones; moderately developed medium prismatic structure; few fine fibrous roots; sharp, irregular boundary.
25+ C(g)2	Reddish brown (5 YR 4/4) clay with prominent grey (5 Y 6/1) mottling on structure faces; occasional medium to large rounded stones; moderately developed medium prismatic structure; roots rare, associated with structure faces; small manganiferous concretions.

PROFILE NO.: La 112, Sollom series, peaty phase; (analysis, p. 92).
Location: Ince Blundell (grid ref. SD 337026).
Relief: flat in gently undulating plain adjacent to mossland.
Altitude: 22 ft. O.D.
Parent Material: Shirdley Hill Sand.
Land Use: ley grassland.
Horizons:
    in.

0–7	Very dark brown (10 YR 2/2) humose loamy sand with many bleached sand grains; weakly developed medium sub-angular blocky and granular structures; friable; abundant small fibrous roots; numerous earthworms; merging, even boundary.

Photograph by K. C Taylor

Plate Ia. View of the Clieves Hills of Triassic Sandstone with soils of the Clive and Crannymoor (rocky phase) series. The gently undulating land in the foreground is on soils of the Sollom complex.

Photograph by K. C. Taylor

Plate Ib. The south-west Lancashire plain from the Clieves Hills looking west towards Formby. Intensive arable farming on soils mainly of the Sollom complex.

Photograph by K. C. Taylor

Plate IIa. Dune sands near Ainsdale. Raw soils on unstable dunes partially colonized by marram grass. Pararendzinas on fixed dunes and micropodzols under the conifers in the background.

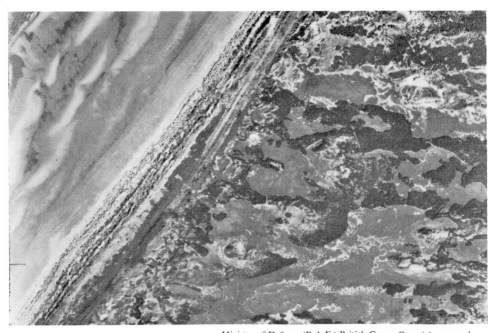

Ministry of Defence (R.A.F.) British Crown Copyright reserved

Plate IIb. Aerial view of the Ainsdale Hills, north of Formby showing well developed swales parallel to the coast. Dark grey areas are of uneven-aged coniferous plantations; medium grey areas are of the Dune Sand complex while unstable dunes are white.

Plate IIIa. Undulating till country in South Fylde near Westby. Salwick and Cottam soils on moderate to gentle slopes with narrow valleys partially infilled with alluvium.

Photograph by K. C. Taylor

Plate IIIb. Reclaimed marsh near Banks with soils of the Hesketh complex used for arable and dairying with livestock rearing. The sea-wall in the distance was built between 1890–95.

Photograph by K. C. Taylor

Plate IVa. Looking south across Halsall Moss; reclaimed mossland under intensive agricultural management.

Plate IVb. The Crossens Pumping Station effectively drains about 32,000 acres of agricultural land in south-west Lancashire. The station houses six 42 in. axial flow pumps of a total capacity of 630 cu. ft./sec.

7–15   Dark brown (7·5 YR 3/2) humose sandy loam with many fine dark reddish brown (2·5 YR 3/4) mottles and bleached sand grains; weakly developed fine sub-angular blocky structure; friable; stoneless; abundant small fibrous roots; numerous earthworms; sharp, even boundary.

15–18   Black (5 YR 2/1) amorphous peat; weakly developed fine angular blocky structure; friable; abundant small fibrous roots; sharp, even boundary.

18–29   Light grey (10 YR 7/2) sand with many distinct dark reddish brown (2·5 YR 3/4) mottles associated with old roots; structureless; loose; merging undulating boundary.

29–40   Light yellowish brown (10 YR 6/4) sand with many distinct dark reddish brown (2·5 YR 3/4) mottles associated with old roots; structureless; loose; sharp, undulating boundary.

40+   Dark greyish brown (2·5 Y 4/2) sand with prominent dark grey (7·5 YR 4/0) mottles associated with old roots; structureless; loose; waterlogged.

CRANNYMOOR SERIES

As previously described a rocky phase of the Crannymoor series is associated with small outcrops of Triassic sandstone on the Formby sheet. Throughout the area covered by Shirdley Hill Sand soils of the Crannymoor series are of very local occurrence and only amount to 420 acres on the Formby sheet and 50 acres on the Southport sheet. Slightly elevated positions in areas dominated by soils of the Sollom complex are invariably occupied by Crannymoor soils, notably on the small dune-like features west of Haskayne. The soils also occur in the Solllom complex where there are no visible features of relief and their presence may well be connected with thicker deposits of sand in depressions of the underlying till surface.

Typical profiles have an A horizon of very dark brown or black humose sand or loamy sand up to 12 in. thick with weakly developed sub-angular blocky and granular or soft crumb structures. Beneath the A horizon there is normally an Ea horizon of light yellowish brown or pale grey structureless sand which varies greatly in thickness. In some instances it may have been entirely incorporated into the surface layer by deep cultivation when its former existence is indicated by the high proportion of bleached sand grains, whilst in others it may be up to 18 in. thick. This is followed by a distinct dark brown or dark reddish brown B horizon of indurated sand which varies from 2 in. to 12 in. in thickness and in position in the profile from within plough depth to below 3 ft. Differentiation of the B horizon into Bh and Bfe horizons is often possible and the lower horizons, with varying degrees of induration, merge into lighter brown structureless sand often with faint brown laminations (*Plate Va*). The sand becomes progressively paler with depth and the reddish brown till is not generally encountered within 3 ft. of the surface.

Drainage is free in the surface horizons but the presence of till restricts water movement in the lower parts of the profile.

The black or very dark brown colouration typical of the A horizon suggests that the amount of organic matter should be greater than indicated by analysis. The loss on ignition, however, is about 5 per cent. and the dark colour is often only staining on the sand grains. In the remainder of the profile the organic-matter content is extremely low, the loss on ignition figures often being less than 1 per cent. Where, however, a Bh horizon is present the value shows a slight rise to 2 or 3 per cent.

4

The soils are naturally acid, with pH values about 5·0–5·5 in the surface horizon rising to about 6·0 in the lowest horizon, and are also very low in plant nutrients especially potash. The ease and rapidity of leaching necessitates frequent and regular applications of lime and fertilizers if high productivity is to be maintained. The cation-exchange capacity decreases sharply from 8 m.e./100 g. at the surface to 1 m.e./100 g. in the Ea horizon with an increase to 5 m.e./100 g. in the Bh horizon.

The cemented B horizons when occurring at no great depth do not permit deep penetration by roots and plants suffer from drought during dry periods. Since the Crannymoor series only occurs as small patches within the areas of the very productive Sollom complex it is invariably managed under the prevailing system of intensive farming although as a soil it must be considered of lower productivity.

Description of a representative profile

PROFILE NO.: La 89, Crannymoor series; (analysis, p. 88).
Location: Downholland Cross (grid ref. SD 354069).
Relief: even slope in very gently undulating plain.
Slope: 2°. *Aspect:* west. *Altitude:* 25 ft. O.D.
Parent Material: Shirdley Hill Sand overlying fine-textured till.
Land Use: ley grassland.
Horizons:

	in.	
0–6 Ap	Black (10 YR 2/1) humose sand with many bleached sand grains; occasional small rounded stones and cinders; weakly developed medium crumb structure; friable; moderate content of organic matter; fine fibrous roots common; occasional earthworms; sharp, irregular boundary.
6–9 Ea	Light yellowish brown (10 YR 6/4) sand with few faint grey mottles; stoneless; structureless; loose; very low organic-matter content which is mainly confined to earthworm channels, few fine fibrous roots, living and dead; sharp, irregular boundary.
9–10 Bh	Dark reddish brown (5 YR 2/2) sand; stoneless; structureless; strongly cemented; low organic-matter content, roots and earthworms absent; sharp, irregular boundary.
10–18 Bhfe1	Dark reddish brown (5 YR 3/4) sand with few large distinct black mottles; stoneless; structureless; weakly cemented; very low organic-matter content; merging, irregular boundary.
18–27 Bhfe2	Dark reddish brown (5 YR 3/2) sand with few medium faint black mottles; stoneless; structureless; weakly cemented; very low organic-matter content; merging, irregular boundary.
27+ C(g)	Dark yellowish brown (10 YR 4/4) sand; stoneless; structureless; loose; very low organic-matter content; water-table at 30 in., 24.2.59.

The area covered by Shirdley Hill Sand is intensively farmed with cereals, roots and brassicas as the principal crops (*Plate I*). The soils are inherently of low fertility and are naturally acid but these defects are largely overcome by the management practices on an easily cultivated medium that is now well drained artificially. Ground limestone is commonly applied at the rate of 2–3 tons per acre every 3 years and annual heavy dressings, up to 20 cwts per acre, are given of a compound fertilizer often chosen for its high potash content. The necessity for drainage is self-evident in the Sollom complex and Rufford series where the presence of till at no great depth and the lack of lateral water movement downslope frequently results in waterlogging in the profile immediately above the junction of the sand and clay. Mechanical analysis shows complete dominance of the sand fraction throughout the profile and where any appreciable quantity of clay occurs in the surface horizon it can be attributed to the former practice of marling. As the amount of clay is low the loss on ignition figures can be used to make a good estimate of the organic-matter content. In most of the soils developed on the Shirdley Hill Sand, the amount of organic matter is low or moderate and the cation-exchange capacity is correspondingly small; where the content of organic matter is greater, the increase in the cation-exchange capacity is most marked. As a result of the low clay content the structures of the surface soil are weak and easily destroyed and, if the land were not level, erosion could be a serious hazard. Even so, wind-blowing of the surface soil can create difficulties, though it rarely occurs.

The almost complete dominance of arable farming and the lack of livestock has resulted in the use of large amounts of artificial fertilizers as a substitute for the nutrients in farmyard manure. In time, this practice could well lead to a dangerous breakdown of the soil structure which the added organic matter had helped to stabilize.

Shirdley Hill Sand forms an extremely valuable deposit of the raw material for the glass industry concentrated in St. Helens. Siliceous sand of sufficient purity, correct grain size and aluminium content is of small extent and suitable deposits are therefore valuable. The bleached sand layers of the gley podzol and the humus-iron podzol have these desirable properties and the soils are exploited for this purpose. The top-soil is stripped and the bleached horizon, which ranges in thickness from 6–36 in., is removed for glass making. After the laying of a tile drainage system and replacement of the top-soil, the land is returned to agriculture.

SOILS FROM RECENT BLOWN SAND

Extensive belts of blown sand, covering about 22 per cent. of the area surveyed, occur along the coastline north of the Ribble between Lytham St. Anne's and South Shore, Blackpool, and south of the estuary between Southport and Great Crosby. The sand attains its greatest width of approximately 3 miles in the vicinity of Formby. In many places the sand is still mobile but elsewhere it is fixed by vegetation; it is mapped as Dune Sand and the Formby series. The Dune Sand includes skeletal soils formed on the naturally unstable, young and mobile dunes, devoid of a continuous vegetative covering; pararendzinas on dunes stabilized by surface vegetation, and ground-water gley soils in the shallow depressions between the lines of dunes. Where the fixed dunes have been planted with conifers micro-podzols have developed under the deep accumulation of plant litter.

Landward of the zone of dunes the blown sand is level and slopes gently eastward until it finally thins out over peat. The soils are mainly ground-water gley soils of the Formby series. Borings and excavations (Wray and Cope, 1948) have established that much of the coastal belt of blown sand is underlain by peat, but during the soil survey it has only been possible to record those areas where the peat occurs within 3 ft. of the surface and to map them as a shallow phase of the Formby series.

DUNE SAND

The unstable dunes, rising in places to about 55 ft. O.D., are composed of non-coherent, calcareous sand, with a high proportion of very fine shell fragments and are only sporadically colonized by marram grass (*Ammophila arenaria*) and lyme-grass (*Elymus arenarius*). Their shapes and sizes are constantly changing under the action of the wind and wind erosion is only halted when the surface nearly reaches the water-table when small, often oval, flat-bottomed hollows (slacks) are formed. Similar, but considerably longer, hollows (swales) are formed by the enclosure of widths of the shore between newly-formed dunes (*Plate IIb*). Swales commonly occur north of Formby Point where accretion is active. Both slacks and swales are affected by fluctuations of the water-table and are frequently flooded so that a thin layer of peat forms above grey, humus-stained, waterlogged sand. It is impracticable to delimit these areas on the published map and they are included in the Dune Sand.

On stable or fixed dunes, rising in places to over 80 ft. O.D. the cover of vegetation is more or less complete and, as shown in profile SD 31/0517, an A horizon between 3 and 8 in. thick is commonly found. Depending on the age of the dune, the horizon contains moderate to low amounts of organic matter, but insufficient to promote noticeable structural development. The A horizon merges into unaltered calcareous dune sand identical with that of the unstable dunes. These immature soils may be regarded as pararendzinas. The calcium-carbonate content of the A horizon decreases with the increasing age of the dunes and the content of organic matter, indicated by the loss on ignition after correction for the amount of carbonate, increases with age.

TABLE 10

Calcium carbonate and Organic-matter Content in relation to Age of Dune

	$CaCO_3$ %	Maturity of Dunes	Organic-matter Content % (Loss on Ignition)
Unstable dunes Sampling depth 0–3 in.	2·7	Juvenile	0·4
Fixed dunes Sampling depth 0–3 in.	1·1	Mature	2·9
	Trace	Old	4·5

Plantations of Scots pine (*Pinus sylvestris*), Corsican pine (*Pinus nigra* var. *calabrica*) and Austrian pine (*Pinus nigra* var. *austriaca*), both pure and in mixture have been established on the fixed dunes between Ainsdale and Hightown. Under the older stands, dating from about 1900, with a complete canopy, the thickness of the litter layer depends to some extent on the conditions within the stand, the thickest layers being found in hollows and on the sheltered sides of dunes. On the tops of dunes and other places exposed to wind erosion the litter is thinner. Accumulations of this organic material may be 6 in. or more thick, consisting of the recently fallen litter (L layer) overlying well developed layers of progressive decomposition (F and H layers). Beneath these thicker organic horizons, thin Ea horizons of acid, bleached grey sand, rarely more than $\frac{1}{2}$ in.

thick are found. Since the amount of iron in the dune sand is small B horizons cannot be discerned. Such soils are regarded as weakly developed podzols.

The effect of coastal position on the plantations is well demonstrated by the severe wind pruning and premature death of trees on the seaward side. Wind and rain from the sea might be expected to carry salt which would be deposited on the litter. An examination of the pine needle litter from Formby gave the following amounts of chloride: L layer 0·2 per cent., F layer 0·13 per cent., H layer 0·06 per cent.; the Ea horizon contained 0·01 per cent. Similar litter from Cannock Chase, Staffordshire was analysed for comparison but only in the L layer was any chloride present (0·03 per cent.) the F, H and Ea horizons containing only traces.

Descriptions of representative profiles

PROFILE NO.: SD 21/9415, Dune Sand (unstable dune).
Location: Formby (grid ref. SD 294115).
Relief: strongly undulating unstable dunes.
Slope: 15°. *Aspect:* west. *Altitude:* 50 ft. O.D.
Parent Material: recent blown sand.
Land Use: amenity purposes; agriculturally unproductive, occasional marram grass and lyme-grass.
Horizons:

in.
0–36+ Light yellowish brown (10 YR 6/4) sand; stoneless; structureless; loose; porous and rapidly permeable; some fine shell fragments; calcareous; very low organic-matter content.

PROFILE NO.: SD 31/0517, Dune Sand (fixed dune).
Location: Formby (grid ref. SD 305117).
Relief: strongly undulating fixed dunes.
Slope: 10°. *Aspect:* north. *Altitude:* 65 ft. O.D.
Parent Material: recent blown sand.
Land Use: agriculturally unproductive with dewberry (*Rubus caesius*) dominant.
Horizons:

in.
0–8   Greyish brown (10 YR 5/2) sand; stoneless; structureless; loose; porous
A   and rapidly permeable; occasional fine shell fragments towards base of horizon; abundant fine and small fibrous and fleshy roots, moderate organic-matter content; merging, undulating boundary.
8+   Light yellowish brown (10 YR 6/4) sand; stoneless; structureless; loose;
C   porous and readily permeable; some fine shell fragments; calcareous; few fine and small fibrous roots becoming rare with depth, very low content of organic matter.

FORMBY SERIES

Immediately inland from the Dune Sand the relief changes abruptly to an extensive, flat terrain of blown sand that is well developed north of Lytham St. Anne's and near Formby and on which the Formby series is found.

This series covers 3,960 acres on the Formby sheet along a coastal belt of variable width between Churchtown and Great Crosby, and 2,430 acres on the Southport sheet between Lytham St. Anne's and South Shore, Blackpool. The soils occupy flat tracts between 15 and 35 ft. O.D. with scarcely perceptible gradients, and are bounded to the west by the strongly undulating dunes and pass eastward into organic or alluvial soils. The profile drainage is normally free above the water-table. The soils are classified as ground-water gley soils in which seasonal fluctuations of the water-table result in the formation of a zone where conditions of alternating reduction and oxidation produce intense orange and rust-brown mottling and iron concretions. This zone overlies the grey, structureless, sand that is permanently waterlogged.

The profiles (*Plate Vc*) are characterized by a dark brown to brown A horizon of sand 5–9 in. thick with very weakly developed granular structures. The organic-matter content in the surface horizon under old pasture is moderate to high and often mat formation is pronounced, but under arable cropping it can become extremely low. The Bg horizon into which the A horizon merges is a yellowish brown sand, stoneless and structureless, with prominent yellowish red and grey mottles and ferruginous concretions. The underlying Cg horizon consists of light yellowish brown or grey, structureless sand that is permanently waterlogged. The surface soil is moderately to strongly acid and the cation-exchange capacity and the content of exchangeable bases are extremely low, that of calcium increasing slightly with depth.

A shallow phase of the Formby series is mapped where peat occurs within 3 ft. of the surface.

Descriptions of representative profiles

PROFILE NO.: La 92, Formby series; (analysis, p. 90).
Location: Formby (grid ref. SD 306094).
Relief: flat.
Altitude: 22 ft. O.D.
Parent Material: recent blown sand.
Land Use: permanent pasture.
Horizons:

in.		
0–1½ A		Dark brown (10 YR 4/3) sand with many bleached sand grains; stoneless; structureless; loose; very porous; abundant fine fibrous roots, living and dead forming a mat, high organic-matter content; few old earthworm channels; merging, undulating boundary.
1½–5½ A(g)		Brown (10 YR 5/3) sand with many distinct fine yellowish red (5 YR 5/8) mottles associated with dead roots; stoneless; structureless; loose; low organic-matter content, many fine fibrous living and dead roots; merging, undulating boundary.
5½–8½ Bg1		Yellowish brown (10 YR 5/4) sand with many prominent medium yellowish red (5 YR 4/8) mottles; stoneless; structureless; loose; low organic-matter content, few fine fibrous living and dead roots; sharp, irregular boundary.
8½–15 Bg2		Yellowish brown (10 YR 5/4) sand with many distinct grey and yellowish red mottles; stoneless; structureless; loose; low organic-matter content confined to old root channels, few fine living and dead roots; sharp, irregular boundary.
15–30 Cg		Light yellowish brown (10 YR 6/2) sand; stoneless; structureless; loose; very low organic-matter content, few fine dead roots; sharp, even boundary.
30+		Light olive-grey (5 Y 6/2) sand; stoneless; structureless; loose; water-table at 36 in. March 2nd 1959.

PROFILE NO.: La 109, Formby series, shallow phase over peat; (analysis, p. 90).
Location: Hightown (grid ref. SD 308032).
Relief: flat.

Altitude: 18 ft. O.D.
Parent Material: recent blown sand.
Land Use: ley grassland.
Horizons:

in.

0–6 A	Very dark greyish brown (10 YR 3/2) sand with distinct yellowish red (5 YR 4/8) mottles at base of horizon; stoneless; weakly developed medium granular structure; very friable; moderate organic-matter content, fine fibrous roots common; occasional earthworms; sharp, irregular boundary.
6–9 Bg	Very dark grey (10 YR 3/1) sand; stoneless; structureless; loose; moderate amount of organic-matter, few fine fibrous roots; occasional old earthworm channels; sharp, even boundary.
9–14 Cg	Yellowish brown (10 YR 5/4) sand with black (2·5 Y 2/0) streaks of organic staining and strong brown (7·5 YR 5/8) mottles; stoneless; structureless; loose; low organic-matter content; sharp, undulating boundary.
14–17	Black (5 YR 2/1) amorphous peat.
17–84	Yellowish brown fibrous fen peat.
84+	Grey (5 Y 6/1) silty clay (Downholland Silt).

The Dune Sand is agriculturally unimportant apart from the coniferous plantations on the fixed dunes and the small, but well known, asparagus-growing industry near Formby. The asparagus beds are constructed by levelling the dunes and the profiles then resemble those of the Formby series, with a fluctuating ground-water table, extremely low organic-matter content, single-grain structure and sand textures. The Formby series is a ground-water gley soil of inherently low fertility and is generally under permanent grassland. Where arable cropping is practised the soils demand careful husbandry in manuring and crop rotation because the excessive leaching leads to a considerable loss of nutrients that must be remedied by frequent applications of lime and fertilizers. Farmyard manure or other organic manures are extremely beneficial for the soil tends to suffer from drought during long dry periods because of the low water-holding capacity of the surface horizons. However, in the shallow phase the underlying peat, within 3 ft. of the surface, holds a reserve of moisture, easily within reach of most plant roots and dryness is rarely a limiting factor for plant growth.

The recreational needs of Southport, Formby, Liverpool, Blackpool and Lytham St. Anne's are such that the Dune Sand area is used primarily for amenity purposes with a concentration of golf courses on soils that are ideally suited for the purpose. Parts of Lytham St. Anne's, Southport and Ainsdale are sited within the Dune Sand, and the densest and most recent urban development has taken place on the level areas. The aerodromes at Woodvale, near Ainsdale and Squires Gate, Blackpool, are also situated on the extensive flat areas where the soils of the Formby series are of low agricultural potential.

It appears that the plant communities on recent blown sand fall within the normal sand dune succession in passing from the foreshore, through the mosaic of unstable dunes and dune slacks to stable or fixed dunes, dune pasture and, in places, dune heath, but nowhere is there evidence of the establishment of pine-heath. The ground flora communities have been described using the Braun–Blanquet system (1932).

Two slacks were sampled, one considered relatively dry, the other wet. Creeping willow (*Salix repens*), early hair-grass (*Aira praecox*), variegated horsetail (*Equisetum variegatum*), common sedge (*Carex nigra*) and sand sedge(*Carex arenaria*) were dominant in both dry and wet slacks. Jointed rush (*Juncus articulatus*), many stemmed spike-rush (*Eleocharia multicaulis*), creeping fescue (*Festuca rubra*) and *Bryum* spp. were also dominant in the dry slack which contained the following additional species: sea buckthorn (*Hippophaë rhamnoides*), water mint (*Mentha aquatica*), pennywort (*Hydrocotyle vulgaris*) brookweed (*Samolus valerandi*), lesser spearwort (*Ranunculus flammula*), and the moss *Hylocomium loreum*. Most of these appear to owe their presence to local areas of increased wetness.

Other species dominant in the wet slack were pennywort, water mint, fiorin (*Agrostis stolonifera*), common horsetail (*Equisetum arvense*) and the mosses *Hypnum cuspidatum* and *Hylocomium loreum*. Additional species, most of which are found around the drier margin of the slack, were: grass of parnassus (*Parnassia palustris*), marsh bedstraw (*Galium palustre*), birdsfoot-trefoil (*Lotus corniculatus*), larger wintergreen (*Pyrola rotundifolia*), self-heal (*Prunella vulgaris*), yellow-wort (*Blackstonia perfoliata*), bog pimpernel (*Anagallis tenella*).

The stable dunes have a more or less complete cover of vegetation, the principal species of which appear to vary according to the height of the dunes and their proximity to the slacks. As well as the community dominated by dewberry (*Rubus caesius*) others on the lower dunes adjacent to the slacks, were found to be dominated by creeping willow. Additional species found locally in some abundance in the stable dune area are:—restharrow (*Ononis repens*), birdsfoot-trefoil, wall-pepper (*Sedum acre*), cat's ear (*Hypochaeris radicata*), rough hawkbit (*Leontodon hispidus*), kidney-vetch (*Anthyllis vulneraria*), common centaury (*Centaurium minus*), lesser knapweed (*Centaurea nigra*), spear thistle (*Cirsium vulgare*), Yorkshire fog, marram grass, ragwort (*Senecio jacobaea*), sweet vernal-grass (*Anthoxanthum odoratum*) and species of wild rose.

The soils on the extensive flat areas in the lee of the dunes have largely been maintained throughout living memory as permanent pasture, which appears to represent a biotic climax. One such pasture has been described in detail. The sward is dominated by sheep's fescue with common bent-grass and sorrel (*Rumex acetosa*) becoming locally abundant. Only a few other species are to be found, namely:—mat grass (*Nardus stricta*), sweet vernal, Yorkshire fog and sand sedge.

One small patch protected from grazing now supports dune heath, the vegetation being dominated by heather (*Calluna vulgaris*), sheep's fescue, creeping fescue and creeping soft-grass (*Holcus mollis*) and apparently indicates the sort of change that might be expected should the grazing on the pastures be stopped.

CHAPTER IV

Soils from Till

The glacial deposits exposed at the surface consist of till, with small, local patches of sand and gravel and insignificant areas of sand referred to as the Middle Sands. Subdivisions into an Upper and Lower Boulder Clay, separated by Middle Sands have been made by the Geological Survey north of the Ribble, but south of the river the Middle Sands are unknown except within a short distance north of Liverpool where they were recorded during excavations (Roberts, 1871). The Upper and Lower Boulder Clays cannot be distinguished from each other, however, unless their separation by the Middle Sands can be seen. Normally the till is reddish brown or purplish brown in colour with approximately 35 per cent. clay (<2 μ) and 30 per cent. sand (>50 μ), although considerable textural variation occurs within the deposit. It is plastic and tenacious and generally contains a high proportion of rounded and sub-angular stones and boulders. The presence of erratics originating in the Lake District and south-west Scotland indicates the till was deposited by ice moving across Lancashire in a south-easterly direction. The till is typical of that found over much of north-west England, North Wales and the Midlands and also occurs on the east coast of Ireland. The reddish brown colour is due essentially to its derivation mainly from material of the Triassic formation, which underlies the whole district. The presence of fragments of shells and the slightly calcareous nature of the till is a notable feature. Although the surface layers are non-calcareous, probably as a result of long-continued leaching, accumulations of calcium carbonate generally occur at depths between $2\frac{1}{2}$ and 5 ft. as pinkish white concretions or as a deposit of dendritic pattern on structure faces.

North of the Ribble the relief of the till is undulating with ridges and hollows and peat-filled valleys. The Middle Sands are exposed on local hillocks around Westby and Little Plumpton. South of the Ribble, however, the relief is more subdued owing to the presence of the superficial deposits of Shirdley Hill Sand and peat so that the till is only occasionally exposed as isolated ridges and mounds.

For soil mapping purposes the till is separated on a textural basis into two main groups (Crompton, 1966). The mechanical composition of the fine-textured till is dominated by the silt and clay fractions and the texture is usually clay, silty clay or, occasionally, clay loam, while that of the surface soils ranges from clay loam to loam. In the medium-textured till, the sand content is appreciably greater than 35 per cent. and the till is generally of loam or clay loam texture, with occasional areas of sandy loam or sandy clay while textures of the surface soils are mainly loam to sandy loam. South of the Ribble most of the underlying till is fine-textured but extensive contamination by sand blown from the adjacent deposits of Shirdley Hill Sand gives rise to sandy surface horizons with textures ranging from loam to sandy loam. Such areas have, therefore, been included with the medium-textured till for mapping purposes. The genetic relationships

49

between the soil horizons distinguishable in the field are not easily determined and the possibility of lithological discontinuity in a profile makes difficult the identification and therefore the application of symbols to every horizon. The oriented and striated clay revealed by examination of thin sections of the soils suggests that there has been some mechanical eluviation of clay and such horizons could be designated Bt.

Natural Drainage Class	Medium-textured till (sand and silt fractions dominant in the surface horizons)	Fine-textured till (clay and silt fractions dominant in the surface horizons)
Imperfectly drained	Salwick series	Cottam series
Poorly drained	Clifton series	Salop series
Very poorly drained	Lea series	Oaklands series

On both types of till the soils vary from imperfectly to very poorly drained and can be arranged in a sequence according to the natural drainage classes; freely drained soils have not been observed on either till within the area. The soils developed on the medium-textured till occupy 4,500 acres, more than one half of which consists of the poorly drained soils of the Clifton series. The fine-textured till only covers 700 acres on the two sheets, 500 acres being poorly drained soils of the Salop series. The imperfectly drained soils of the Salwick and Cottam series are classified as gleyed brown earths and occur on shedding sites the slopes of which generally do not exceed 4° and are commonly about 2°. This degree of slope allows considerable lateral flow of water on the surface and the irregularity of the undulating relief causes the run-off to flow in many directions. The Clifton and Salop series occur on flat sites or on slopes not exceeding 2° that receive water from higher land and the soils are frequently found at the foot of slopes occupied by soils of the Salwick and Cottam series. The Clifton and Salop series are regarded as surface-water gley soils while the Lea and Oaklands series, differentiated as the very poorly drained members of the two sequences, are described as humic gley soils. The latter series occur on extensive flat areas with little or no lateral drainage, in basin sites and adjacent to the peat.

SALWICK SERIES

The soils of this series, covering 770 acres on the Southport sheet and 210 acres on the Formby sheet, are developed on medium-textured till and are regarded as gleyed brown earths. The relief is undulating with gentle to medium slopes where the site drainage is usually satisfactory (*Plate IIIa*) and profile drainage is generally imperfect.

The dark brown or greyish brown surface layer, sometimes slightly rust mottled, of sandy loam or loam texture and generally with moderately developed, sub-angular blocky and granular structures, merges into a brown Eb(g) horizon of similar texture and sub-angular blocky structure with faint yellowish brown and grey mottles. Towards the base the colours generally become brighter and the mottling is more distinct, the structure changes to weakly developed medium prismatic, the texture becomes sandy clay loam and the horizon can be designated Bt(g). The Bt(g) and Cg horizons are not sharply differentiated but the change is marked by an increase in the size and degree of development of the structural units. The colour of the Cg horizon is dominantly reddish brown and a zone where calcium carbonate has accumulated in the form either of small pinkish concretions or of a dendritic pattern on structural faces often occurs between 36 and 60 in.

Description of a representative profile

PROFILE NO.: La 100, Salwick series; (analysis, p. 92).
Location: Clieves Hills (grid ref. SD 388073).
Relief: minor ridge on gently undulating plain.
Slope: 2°. *Aspect:* south. *Altitude:* 175 ft. O.D.
Parent Material: medium-textured till.
Land Use: ley grassland.
Horizons:

in.	
0–5 Ap	Dark brown (7·5 YR 3/2) stony sandy loam with few bleached sand grains; fine to medium sub-angular blocky and granular structures; friable; moderate organic-matter content, numerous fine roots; numerous earthworms; merging, even boundary.
5–10 A	Brown to dark brown (7·5 YR 4/2) stony sandy loam; medium sub-angular blocky structure; fine pores and fissures; firm; moderate organic-matter content, numerous fine roots; numerous earthworms; merging, even boundary.
10–15 Eb(g)	Brown (7·5 YR 5/4) stony sandy loam with faint yellowish brown and grey mottles; medium to coarse sub-angular blocky structure; fine pores and fissures; firm; moderate organic-matter content, small roots common; occasional earthworms; sharp irregular boundary.
15–18 Bt(g)	Yellowish red (5 YR 4/6) stony sandy clay loam with distinct yellowish brown mottles; weakly developed medium prismatic structure with distinct grey mottling on faces; fine pores and fissures; firm; moderate organic-matter content associated with old roots and earthworm channels, occasional small roots; numerous small manganiferous concretions; merging, irregular boundary.
18–28 Bt/C(g)	Reddish brown (5 YR 4/4) slightly stony silty clay loam with distinct grey mottling on structure faces and few yellowish brown mottles within the peds; moderately developed coarse prismatic structure; fine pores and fissures; firm; moderate organic-matter content confined to old root and earthworm channels, living roots rare; abundant fine manganiferous concretions; merging, even boundary.
28–40 C(g)	Dark reddish brown (5 YR 3/4) slightly stony silty clay loam with many distinct grey (10 YR 6/1) mottles on structure faces; strongly developed coarse prismatic structure; firm; roots rare; merging irregular boundary.
40+ C(g)ca	Dark reddish brown (5 YR 3/4) slightly stony clay loam with many distinct grey (10 YR 6/1) mottles on structure faces; moderately developed coarse prismatic structure; numerous pinkish concretions of calcium carbonate.

CLIFTON SERIES

There are 1,320 acres shown as the Clifton series on the Southport sheet and 1,310 acres on the Formby sheet. The series is widely distributed in small patches throughout the areas of till both north and south of the Ribble. The soils occur on level ground or on gentle uniform slopes generally not exceeding 2° that receive water from higher land so that both site and profile drainage are poor. The soils are frequently found at the foot of slopes occupied by soils of the Salwick series and represent the surface-water gley soils of the hydrologic sequence.

The parent material is the reddish brown medium-textured till although areas of fine-textured till with some superficial contamination with sand are also included in the series.

A typical profile shows a surface Ag or A(g) horizon, 6 to 8 in. thick, dominantly dark grey or dark greyish brown in colour with some faint mottling of grey and strong brown along root channels. The texture is either sandy loam or loam, occasionally sandy clay loam, and the structures are medium to fine sub-angular blocky and granular or crumb. There is a fairly sharp boundary to the underlying Ebg or Bg horizon which is dull grey or light brownish grey sandy loam to sandy clay loam with weakly developed blocky structures. Towards the base of this horizon, which often extends to about 12 in. a thin Bt(g) horizon may be recognized; the colour becomes yellowish red or strong brown with distinct grey mottling on structure faces and the texture is usually a clay loam or sandy clay loam with weak to moderate prismatic structures. The C(g) horizon of sandy clay loam or clay loam texture is dark reddish brown with many distinct grey mottles on structure faces and within peds. The till is slightly calcareous and a horizon with carbonate accumulation in the form of small concretions occurs between 30 and 60 in.

Description of a representative profile

PROFILE NO.: La 99, Clifton series; (analysis, p. 87).
Location: Halsall Hill (grid ref. SD 376082).
Relief: level site on gently undulating plain.
Altitude: 70 ft. O.D.
Parent Material: medium-textured till.
Land Use: ley grassland.
Horizons:

in.		
0–6 Ap(g)	Very dark greyish brown (10 YR 3/2) slightly stony sandy loam with some fine rusty mottling mainly associated with living roots; medium to fine sub-angular blocky and granular structures; friable; moderate organic-matter content, numerous fine roots; numerous earthworms; recently limed; sharp, undulating boundary.	
6–10 Bg or Ebg	Light brownish grey (10 YR 6/2) slightly stony sandy loam with dull reddish brown mottles; weakly developed medium blocky structure; friable; moderate organic-matter content, mainly associated with worm channels, numerous fine roots; sharp, undulating boundary.	
10–12 Bt(g)	Strong brown (7·5 YR 5/6) slightly stony clay loam with grey (5 Y 6/1) structure faces; moderately developed prismatic structure separated by wide fissures; firm; moderate organic-matter content mainly as stains on ped faces, few fine roots; occasional earthworm channels; merging, irregular boundary.	
12–32 C(g)	Dark reddish brown (5 YR 3/4) slightly stony clay loam with many fine grey (10 YR 6/1) mottles on structure faces; moderately developed medium to coarse prismatic structure; moderate organic-matter content associated with ped faces and the walls of root channels; roots rare; merging, irregular boundary.	

32+   Dark reddish brown (5 YR 3/4) slightly stony clay loam with many medium
C(g)ca to fine grey (10 YR 6/1) mottles on structure faces and within peds;
        moderately developed coarse prismatic structure; moderate organic-matter
        content mainly on ped faces; numerous pinkish concretions and dendrites
        of calcium carbonate on the ped faces.

LEA SERIES

The Lea series is the very poorly drained soil formed on medium-textured till
and is of very restricted occurrence south of the Ribble, only occupying 70
acres; north of the Ribble it is more widespread and covers 870 acres. These
humic gley soils occur either in depressions, or on extensive flat sites on the till
plain, or on the gentle slopes fringing the peat. Site drainage is poor and profile
drainage very poor. The identifying features of the soils are the very dark brown
or very dark grey friable humose or peaty surface layers with well developed
sub-angular blocky and granular or crumb structures overlying the strongly
gleyed Ebg horizon and underlying reddish brown Cg horizon with prominent
grey mottling on the faces of the prismatic structures. Textures of the Ag and
Ebg horizons range from sandy loam to sandy clay loam and structural elements
are only weakly developed. The structures are in strong contrast with the well
developed, coarse prismatic structures of the Cg horizon of sandy clay loam or
clay loam texture. Concretions of calcium carbonate frequently occur between
30 and 60 in. and the till below this depth is slightly calcareous.

Description of a representative profile

PROFILE NO.: La 121, Lea series; (analysis, p. 91).
Location: Peel Hill Bridge (grid ref. SD 356325).
Relief: small depression in gently undulating plain.
Altitude: 50 ft. O.D.
Parent Material: medium-textured till.
Land Use: permanent grassland.
Horizons:

in.

0–8   Very dark brown (10 YR 2/2) slightly stony humose clay loam with dark
Ag   yellowish brown (10 YR 4/4) mottles associated with roots and structure
        faces; moderately developed medium to fine sub-angular blocky and
        granular structures; friable; abundant fine and small roots; numerous
        earthworms; sharp, irregular boundary.
8–21   Light brownish grey (2·5 Y 6/2) stony sandy loam with distinct brownish
Ebg   yellow (10 YR 6/8) and dark grey (10 YR 4/1) mottles associated with old
        roots; weakly developed medium to fine sub-angular blocky structures;
        friable; low organic-matter content mainly associated with old root chan-
        nels; roots rare and confined to the top of the horizon; sharp, irregular
        boundary.
21+   Reddish brown (5 YR 4/3) stony clay loam with grey (10 YR 5/1) mottling
Cg   on structure faces; strongly developed coarse prismatic structure; firm;
        moderate amount of organic matter associated with structure faces and old
        root channels; some manganiferous staining in fissures.

COTTAM SERIES

This series, covering 70 acres on the Southport sheet and 30 acres on the Formby
sheet, is widely distributed in small patches associated with the till ridges. The
relief is undulating with the series occupying the gentle slopes (*Plate IIIa*).

Site drainage is satisfactory and profile drainage imperfect. The parent material of the soil is the reddish brown fine-textured till.

The A (g) horizon is a brown to dark greyish brown friable silt loam or loam, often with faint yellowish red mottles, and having fine sub-angular blocky and granular structures. This merges at about 8 in. into a dark greyish brown or brown A(g) or Eb(g) horizon, distinctly mottled with strong brown, which is usually of loam or clay loam texture and has weakly developed blocky and prismatic structures. The colour of the succeeding Bt(g) horizon changes to strong brown with distinct grey and dark brown mottles on structure faces and moderate development of prismatic structures. At variable depths but generally below 30 in. the Bt(g) horizon passes to the reddish brown clay or clay loam of the Cg horizon with prominent grey mottles on structure faces. At depths between 36 and 60 in. calcium carbonate usually occurs either as small pinkish white concretions or as a deposit of dendritic pattern on the structure faces.

Description of a representative profile

PROFILE NO.: La 108, Cottam series; (analysis, p. 87).
Location: Higher Ballam (grid ref. SD 378294).
Relief: even slope in gently undulating plain.
Slope: 2°. *Aspect:* west. *Altitude:* 22 ft. O.D.
Parent Material: fine-textured till.
Land Use: permanent grassland.
Horizons:
in.

0–7 A(g)	Dark brown (7·5 YR 3/2) slightly stony loam with many fine yellowish red (5 YR 4/8) mottles; fine sub-angular blocky and granular structures; friable; high organic-matter content, numerous fine roots; numerous earthworms; merging, irregular boundary.
7–22 A(g) or Eb(g)	Dark greyish brown (10 YR 4/2) loam with many distinct strong brown (7·5 YR 5/6) mottles; occasional medium to large rounded stones; weakly developed blocky and prismatic structures; firm; moderate organic-matter content; common fine roots; occasional earthworms; merging, irregular boundary.
22–32 Bt(g)	Strong brown (7·5 YR 5/6) clay loam with dark grey (10 YR 4/1) and brown (7·5 YR 4/2) mottles on structure faces; occasional medium to large rounded stones; weakly developed prismatic structures; moderate organic-matter content associated with root and worm channels, few fine roots; occasional earthworms; merging, irregular boundary.
32–48 C(g)	Reddish brown (5 YR 4/3) clay loam with grey (5 Y 5/1) structure faces; occasional medium to large rounded stones; moderately developed prismatic structure; moderate organic-matter content associated with old root channels, roots very rare; small manganiferous concretions; merging, irregular boundary.
48+ C(g)ca	Brown (7·5 YR 4/4) clay with dark grey (5 Y 4/1) mottling on structure faces; occasional medium to large rounded stones; moderately developed prismatic structure; plastic; abundant calcium carbonate concretions.

SALOP SERIES

Salop soils, as mapped originally in Flintshire and Anglesey (Hughes and Walters, 1932, 1935) and in Shropshire (Crompton and Osmond, 1954) include both imperfectly and poorly drained soils. The former are now separated as the Cottam series while the poorly drained soils are recognized as the Salop series,

90 acres of which have been mapped on the Southport sheet and 440 acres on the Formby sheet. The Salop series is found on sites with relief similar to that of the Clifton series, *i.e.* flat areas or gentle slopes, and the natural drainage is poor because of the combination of slow run-off and low permeability of the profile. The parent material is the reddish brown fine-textured till containing many sub-angular stones of mixed origin.

The friable dark brown or dark greyish brown A(g) horizon, with fine rusty mottling common along root channels and loam or silt loam texture passes into the Ag or Ebg horizon which is greyish brown or light brownish grey, mottled loam or clay loam with a weakly developed angular blocky structure. Beneath it appears a Btg horizon of reddish brown clay with strongly developed prismatic structures with grey and rust mottles on the faces. This merges into the prismatic-structured Cg horizon of reddish brown firm clay or clay loam with prominent grey and dark brown mottling on the structure faces. At depths of between 30 and 60 in. calcium carbonate frequently occurs as a white dendritic deposit or as pinkish white concretions and below this horizon the till is generally slightly calcareous.

Description of a representative profile

PROFILE NO.: La 131, Salop series; (analysis, p. 91).
Location: Hutton (grid ref. SD 514266).
Slope: 2°. *Aspect:* south. *Altitude:* 85 ft. O.D.
Parent Material: fine-textured till.
Land Use: permanent grassland.
Horizons:

in.

0–6 A(g)	Very dark greyish brown (10 YR 3/2) slightly stony loam with few fine rusty mottles; weakly developed fine to medium sub-angular blocky and granular structures; friable; moderate organic-matter content, abundant fine roots; numerous earthworms; sharp, irregular boundary.
6–13 Ag or Ebg	Light brownish grey (10 YR 6/2) stony loam with few dark grey (5 Y 4/1) and rusty mottles; weakly developed medium angular blocky structure; firm; moderate amount of organic matter, few small roots; occasional earthworms; merging, even boundary.
13–21 Btg	Dark reddish grey (5 YR 4/2) slightly stony clay with few grey (5 Y 5/1) and dark brown (7·5 YR 4/2) mottles on structure faces; strongly developed coarse prismatic structure; firm; moderate organic-matter content mainly associated with structure faces, few small roots chiefly in fissures; occasional worm tracks; merging, irregular boundary.
21–42 C(g)	Brown (7·5 YR 4/4) slightly stony clay with prominent dark grey (5 Y 4/1) mottling on structure faces; strongly developed coarse prismatic structure; firm; moderate organic-matter content mainly associated with structure faces and in root and earthworm channels, few small roots chiefly in fissures; occasional worm tracks; merging, irregular boundary.
42+ C(g)ca	Dark reddish brown (5 YR 3/4) slightly stony clay with prominent dark grey (5 YR 4/1) mottles on structure faces; strongly developed coarse prismatic structure; firm; roots very rare; pinkish calcium carbonate concretions common.

OAKLANDS SERIES

The soils of the Oaklands series only cover 15 acres on the Formby sheet and 90 acres on the Southport sheet. They are developed on fine-textured till and represent the very poorly drained member of the catenary sequence. The soils are found on sites with relief similar to those of the Lea series.

A typical profile shows a very dark brown or black Ag horizon of humose or peaty silt loam or loam with moderately well developed fine angular blocky and granular structures, sometimes crumb, passing clearly into a Bg horizon, dark grey in colour with distinct brownish yellow mottles occurring along root channels. The texture is invariably silty clay loam and the structure medium to coarse prismatic. The Bg horizon merges into the silty clay Cg horizon which is reddish brown in colour with distinct grey mottles on the prismatic structure faces and on many old root channels. Calcium carbonate, in the form of concretions and dendritic deposits on structure faces occurs between 30 and 60 in. and below this the till is slightly calcareous.

Description of a representative profile

PROFILE NO.: SD 52/1465, Oaklands series; (analysis, p. 91).
Location: Hutton (grid ref. SD 514265).
Relief: small depression in gently undulating plain.
Altitude: 80 ft. O.D.
Parent Material: fine-textured till.
Land Use: permanent grassland.
Horizons:

in.	
0–11 Ag	Very dark brown (10 YR 2/2) slightly stony humose clay; moderately developed fine angular blocky and granular structures; friable; abundant fine and small roots; frequent earthworms; sharp, even boundary.
11–16 Btg or Bg	Dark grey (10 YR 4/1) stony clay with brownish yellow (10 YR 6/8) mottles associated with roots; strongly developed coarse prismatic structure; very firm; moderate organic-matter content, roots rare; merging, even boundary.
16–36 Cgca	Reddish brown (5 YR 4/3) slightly stony clay with grey (5 YR 5/1) mottles on structure faces and root channels; strongly developed coarse prismatic structure; very firm; moderate organic-matter content largely associated with structure faces and old root channels, roots very rare; a few pinkish calcium carbonate concretions at the base of the horizon.

In all the series formed on till the pH values increase with depth and, if allowance is made for the effect of liming on the surface soils, the pH values, exchangeable calcium and percentage saturation figures demonstrate the loss of calcium from the surface layers; both the gradual increase in amount of calcium carbonate towards the base of the profile and the form of the carbonate suggest it is of secondary accumulation. The Cottam soil (profile La 108) with calcium carbonate percentage of 15·2 and a pH value of 8·3 in the Cgca horizon between 48 and 58 in. emphasizes the calcareous nature of the clay in this horizon.

The soils have marked structural profiles and mechanical analyses show that the clay content generally increases down the profile or attains a maximum value that suggests either a lithological discontinuity or clay illuviation or both. In view of the geological history the first possibility cannot be overlooked. The examination of thin sections of the soil from the various horizons, however, reveals that the sand grains in the B and C horizons are generally coated with strongly oriented and striated clay, suggesting that clay has been washed out of the surface layers and deposited around the grains at lower levels.

Photograph by K. C Taylor

Plate Ia. View of the Clieves Hills of Triassic Sandstone with soils of the Clive and Crannymoor (rocky phase) series. The gently undulating land in the foreground is on soils of the Sollom complex.

Photograph by K. C. Taylor

Plate Ib. The south-west Lancashire plain from the Clieves Hills looking west towards Formby. Intensive arable farming on soils mainly of the Sollom complex.

Plate IIa. Dune sands near Ainsdale. Raw soils on unstable dunes partially colonized by marram grass. Pararendzinas on fixed dunes and micropodzols under the conifers in the background.

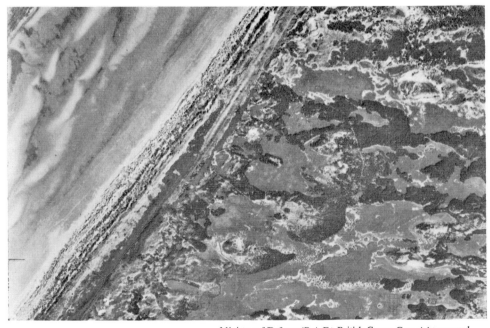

Plate IIb. Aerial view of the Ainsdale Hills, north of Formby showing well developed swales parallel to the coast. Dark grey areas are of uneven-aged coniferous plantations; medium grey areas are of the Dune Sand complex while unstable dunes are white.

Plate IIIa. Undulating till country in South Fylde near Westby. Salwick and Cottam soils on moderate to gentle slopes with narrow valleys partially infilled with alluvium.

Photograph by K. C. Taylor

Plate IIIb. Reclaimed marsh near Banks with soils of the Hesketh complex used for arable and dairying with livestock rearing. The sea-wall in the distance was built between 1890–95.

Photograph by K. C. Taylor

Plate IVa. Looking south across Halsall Moss; reclaimed mossland under intensive agricultural management.

Plate IVb. The Crossens Pumping Station effectively drains about 32,000 acres of agricultural land in south-west Lancashire. The station houses six 42 in. axial flow pumps of a total capacity of 630 cu. ft./sec.

Loss on ignition in the surface horizons of the Salop, Clifton, Cottam and Salwick series indicates a moderate amount of organic matter but there is little in the parent materials. Cation-exchange capacities are moderate and the percentage saturation normally ranges from 40 to 80 per cent. increasing with depth and becoming 100 per cent. in the C horizon. In the humose A horizon of the Lea and Oakland soils the loss on ignition can rise to 60 per cent.; it may decrease to less than 20 per cent. in the less humose soils. These high figures reflect the high content of organic matter with which is associated a high base-exchange capacity.

Natural drainage channels formed by fissures between structural units close during wet periods as the prisms swell, and adequate artificial drainage is, therefore, essential for maximum production especially in the gley and humic gley soils. Mole draining the Cottam, Salop and Oakland soils has proved to be quite effective, the mole being drawn immediately below the pale grey horizon of maximum waterlogging. In the case of the soils formed on medium-textured till (Salwick, Clifton and Lea series) the higher sand content prevents mole draining being satisfactory, and tiles must be used. North of the Ribble there is considerable evidence of the old practice of ridge-and-furrow cultivation that assisted the removal of surface water. Generally the soils formed on till are suited to cereals and grassland and form the basis of the flourishing grassland and dairy farming north of the Ribble. South of the Ribble, however, the tradition of intensive arable farming on the more extensive areas of peat and Shirdley Hill Sand has resulted in the spread of similar enterprises onto soils associated with the till. On the naturally very poorly drained Lea and Oaklands series the high organic-matter content of the surface results in excellent structural development and where the soils have been adequately drained they are frequently utilized for the growing of vegetables and glasshouse crops.

The problems associated with fine-textured till soils are winter compaction and poaching if they are stocked during wet periods and the difficulty in obtaining a good tilth during cultivation.

Only isolated small stands of mature semi-natural deciduous woodland are to be found on till at the present time. They are relics of the predominant moist Oakwood Association which occurred on the finer-textured soils throughout the area. On Salop series at Hutton (grid ref. SD 515267) mixed high forest of uneven age comprising oak, ash (*Fraxinus excelsior*), beech and sycamore has a density of 84 stems per acre with breast-height diameters ranging from 8 to 28 in., maximum height of stand 70 ft., canopy height 30 ft., and canopy density 65 per cent. There is a well developed though patchy understorey of hawthorn (*Crataegus oxyacanthoides*), alder (*Alnus glutinosa*), sycamore, ash and holly ranging in height from 6 ft. to 30 ft. Where mature trees form a closed canopy there is no understorey and the ground-flora is dominated by creeping soft-grass with many oak seedlings and a little ivy (*Hedera helix*). Openings in the canopy are marked by occasional naturally regenerated sycamore and ash, and clumps of elder and beneath this understorey is dense bramble.

5

Soils from Alluvial Deposits

SOILS FROM DOWNHOLLAND SILT

The deposits of variable but mainly fine-textured material situated seawards of the Hillhouse Coastline are referred to as Downholland Silt. Large areas were formerly covered by peat but, by drainage and agricultural use of the land, much peat has disappeared and the underlying deposits are now exposed. The soils developed on it are so variable that it is not practicable to delimit the boundaries of soil series and the soils are mapped as the Downholland complex. The soils cover 4·7 per cent. of the area surveyed on the two sheets, 1,320 acres occurring on the Southport sheet and 1,210 acres on the Formby sheet.

North of the Ribble, the Downholland complex forms an extensive low-lying tract of land between Common Edge and Saltcotes, including Great Marton and Lytham Moss, and is interrupted only by ridges of till and by small areas of peat which overlie the Downholland Silt. South of the Ribble, the complex has been mapped north-east of Hightown and around Great Altcar. These two areas are divided by a wide expanse of more recent alluvium laid down by the Alt, so that the boundary between the deposits is somewhat difficult to ascertain.

Most of the area now occupied by the Downholland complex was formerly covered by peat. The destruction of the peat, attributed to the combined effects of oxidation resulting from intensive cultivation, drainage and, in some localities, peat cutting, has resulted in the exposure of the Downholland Silt at the surface and the restriction of the peat to patches in depressions. The area of the complex is gradually increasing as the destruction of peat continues.

The Downholland complex consists of gley soils and humic or peaty gley soils in which gleying is associated with seasonal fluctuations of the regional ground-water table and, in the fine-textured phases, with the slow percolation of water. Individual series in the complex are closely related to the micro-relief of small ridges and hollows in broad flat tracts of land where elevations rarely exceed 15 ft. O.D. The ridges, for reasons which are not apparent, are often oriented from north-west to south-east. Particularly good examples are to be seen around Great Altcar, north of the road from Formby to Hillhouse, where the distance from crest to crest is approximately 40 yds. and the height is about 3 ft. The ridges are composed of fine sand and contrast strongly with the hollows in which the silt and clay fractions are dominant. Peaty surface soils are well developed in the hollows and humose top soils occur on the ridges. The soils are also clearly distinguished by the amount of calcium carbonate present. The fine-textured deposit in the hollows is non-calcareous and contrasts with the calcareous fine sand (up to 10 per cent. $CaCO_3$) on the ridges. The reasons for this, again, are not apparent but presumably reflect deposition in brackish lagoons on a rapidly emerging beach. The analyses below demonstrate the marked differences both in mechanical composition and carbonate content between the soils on the ridges and in the hollows. The samples were taken at depths between 18 and 22 in.

		Ridges			Hollows		
Coarse sand	%	0	1	0	0	0	0
Fine sand	%	82	83	85	18	26	14
Silt	%	4	3	5	30	34	31
Clay	%	3	5	4	42	31	44
$CaCO_3$	%	9	5	2	0	0	0

It is not possible to depict the distribution of the ridges and hollows with their very different soils and the difficulty is accentuated when attempting to map cultivated areas.

DOWNHOLLAND COMPLEX

For descriptive purposes, the soils of this complex may be divided into three. The first group are coarse to medium textured and occur on the numerous ridges found throughout the complex; they are exemplified by profile La 95. The surface soil is black and humose with textures ranging from loamy fine sand to silt loam. Well developed granular and sub-angular blocky peds are normal but compaction under old pastures frequently leads to the development of somewhat platy structures with associated faint rusty mottling following old roots. The underlying Bg horizon is light grey to light brownish grey in colour with very striking laminations of light grey silt particularly in the lower parts of the horizon. The laminated nature of the uppermost part of the horizon is often indistinct as a result of disturbance by roots and faunal activity and the weak development of angular blocky structures. Prominent rust mottles are frequently associated with large root channels as well as being irregularly distributed throughout the horizon—characters that are typical of horizons subjected to fluctuations of a water-table. Percolation through the A horizon to the zone of water-table fluctuations is, however, rapid at all times. The Bg horizon overlies a strongly gleyed C horizon with only faint rust mottles and a complete lack of organic matter. Although strongly laminated there is no structural development attributable to pedological processes and the parent material consists essentially of sharply separated layers of light grey silt and brownish grey fine sand. The Cg horizon is always wet because the water-table is either in or not far beneath it.

The A horizon is normally neutral or slightly acid but pH values rise sharply in the Bg horizon to between 7·0 and 8·5 and remain high in the Cg horizon. Below the plough layer the profile is highly calcareous throughout and base saturated, the content of calcium carbonate rising as high as 10 per cent. The high cation-exchange capacity of the surface soil is a direct reflection of the high organic-matter content.

Soils of the second group are found in the hollows and on flat land and are formed on fine-textured alluvium composed essentially of silt and clay with insignificant amounts of coarse sand, with surface textures of humose or peaty silt or clay loams (profile La 116). The amount of fine sand, however, increases with depth and, generally below 3 ft., the textures resemble those of the Cg horizon of the first group. Not only is the surface horizon humose, but partly decomposed and strongly iron-stained plant remains are irregularly distributed throughout the profile.

The surface soil is a black or very dark brown humose or peaty silt loam to clay loam with moderately developed fine and medium crumb structure. Abundant ferruginous staining is associated with decomposing plant remains and dead roots. The underlying Bg horizon is a grey silty clay with many prominent yellowish red mottles and numerous ochreous concretions, and with strongly developed blocky and coarse prismatic structures. When moist the soil is both plastic and sticky but it hardens on drying and is very difficult to re-wet. Laminations are completely disrupted by the strong development of prismatic structures but can readily be seen in the underlying Cg horizon. This consists of grey silt loam, with many distinct strong brown mottles, which passes, generally below 3 ft., into clearly alternating bands of silt and fine sand and with textures ranging from silt to loamy fine sand.

Unlike the coarser-textured soils on the ridges the soils are non-calcareous with pH values ranging between 5·0 and 7·0 in the Ag and Bg horizons. The Cg horizon, however, is generally calcareous and the pH values range from 7·5 to 8·5. The cation-exchange capacity is high in the surface layer as a result of the high organic-matter content. Calcium is the dominant exchangeable cation throughout, but the proportion of magnesium increases in the lower horizons.

The third group is confined to the more pronounced hollows in which a thin cover of peat still exists so that the soils when cultivated, are loamy peats or peaty loams with strongly developed granular and crumb structures reminiscent of "skirt" soils adjacent to the main peat deposits. The characteristic feature of this group is the thin layer of peat underlying the Ap horizon (profile La 118). This peat is normally amorphous with moderately developed, medium, angular blocky and granular structures and is rarely more than 3 in. thick. Whether or not it will remain as a distinct layer of undisturbed peat depends on the future depth of ploughing. The peat overlies and is sharply separated from the Cg horizon of grey silty clay with prominent yellowish red mottles and coarse prismatic structures (*Plate VIa*).

The surface horizons of these peaty soils are moderately acid with pH values as low as 5·0 in places and they have very high cation-exchange capacities.

Descriptions of representative profiles

PROFILE NO.: La 95 from the Downholland complex; (analysis, p. 89).
Location: Altcar (grid ref. SD 329066).
Relief: flat with minor ridges and hollows, pit on top of small ridge.
Altitude: 14 ft. O.D.
Parent Material: Downholland Silt.
Land Use: permanent grassland.
Horizons:

in.

0–7
A
Black (10 YR 2/1) humose silt loam with few faint very fine brown mottles associated with dead roots; stoneless; moderately developed fine subangular blocky and fine granular structures; very high organic-matter content, abundant fine fibrous roots; earthworms frequent; sharp, even boundary.

7–9
Bg1
Light brownish grey (2·5 Y 6/2) fine sandy loam with prominent fine and medium brown (10 YR 5/3) mottles; stoneless; weakly developed medium angular blocky structure; laminated; friable; very low organic-matter

	content associated with old root channels, few fine living and dead roots; occasional earthworms; merging, irregular boundary.
9–33	Light brownish grey (2·5 Y 6/2) silt loam with many prominent medium
Bg2	yellowish brown (10 YR 5/6) mottles; stoneless; strongly platy; firm; few medium dead roots; calcareous; sharp, irregular boundary.
33–37	Light grey (5 Y 7/2) silt loam with few faint medium and large strong
Cg	brown (7·5 YR 5/8) mottles associated with dead roots and root channels; stoneless; platy; firm; few medium and large dead roots; calcareous; water-table at 37 in. on March 10th 1959.

PROFILE NO.: La 116 from the Downholland complex; (analysis, p. 89).
Location: Hightown (grid ref. SD 304049).
Relief: flat with minor ridges and hollows, pit in hollow.
Altitude: 13 ft. O.D.
Parent Material: Downholland Silt.
Land Use: ley grassland.
Horizons:
   in.

0–7	Very dark brown (10 YR 2/2) humose clay loam with prominent strong
Apg	brown (7·5 YR 5/6) staining on decomposing plant remains; stoneless; moderately developed fine and medium crumb structures; friable; high organic-matter content, abundant fine fibrous roots; occasional earthworms; fragments of the underlying horizon incorporated into the plough layer by cultivation; sharp, even boundary.
7–17	Grey (5 Y 6/1) silty clay with prominent fine yellowish red (5 YR 4/8)
Bg	mottles associated with old roots and many small and medium ochreous concretions; stoneless; firm; strongly developed blocky and large prismatic structures; moderate organic-matter content, fine fibrous roots common; occasional earthworms; merging, irregular boundary.
17+	Grey (5 Y 6/1) silt loam with prominent medium and large strong brown
Cg	(7·5 YR 5/6) mottles; platy and a few large vertical fissures; plastic; moderate amounts of organic-matter associated with old root channels, few large dead roots; water-table at 27 in. on April 23rd 1959.

PROFILE NO.: La 118 from the Downholland complex; (analysis, p. 89).
Location: Higher Ballam (grid ref. SD 361299).
Relief: flat with minor ridges and hollows; pit dug in hollow.
Altitude: 13 ft. O.D.
Parent Material: Downholland Silt.
Land Use: ley grassland.
Horizons:
   in.

0–8	Very dark brown (10 YR 2/2) humose loam with prominent strong brown
Apg	(7·5 YR 5/6) staining on decomposing plant fragments; moderately developed fine and medium crumb structures; friable; abundant fine and small fibrous roots; numerous earthworms; sharp, even boundary. (Heavily marled in the past.)
8–8½	Dark reddish brown (5 YR 3/3) amorphous peat; stoneless; moderately
C1g	developed medium angular blocky and granular structures; friable; abundant fine fibrous roots; occasional earthworms; sharp, even boundary.
8½+	Grey (5 Y 6/1) silty clay loam with prominent fine yellowish red (5 YR 4/8)
C2g	mottles associated with old root channels; stoneless; firm; strongly developed medium to large blocky and coarse prismatic structures; moderate organic-matter content associated with old root channels; laminated below 18 in.; water-table at 19 in. April 24th 1959.

At present most of the Downholland complex is under intensive arable cultivation but the introduction of grassland farming around Great Altcar raises the question of the possibility of a widespread change in the farming pattern as a consequence of the gradual loss of the peat. The extent of the soils of this complex is gradually increasing because of the intensive arable cultivation of adjoining areas of peat (Altcar complex). North of the Ribble, the peat overlies Downholland Silt and is generally more than 3 ft. thick though it thins out around the edges of Great Marton and Lytham Mosses. The extent of the Downholland deposits underlying peat to the south of the Ribble is shown in Fig. 7. Much of the peat exceeds 3 ft. in thickness and the maximum recorded is 13 ft. but between Ainsdale and Brown Edge (including the western edge of Halsall Moss, Granton Moss and Blowick Moss) and west of Churchtown, on parts of Churchtown Moss, the thickness varies between 1 and 3 ft. Around Great Altcar horizontal bands of silt up to 3 ft. thick occur in deposits of thick peat and many of them occur within 2 ft. of the surface. Under the present farming conditions it is inevitable that peat will continue to disappear and if it is assumed that peat shrinks at the rate of $\frac{1}{4}$ to $\frac{1}{2}$ in. per annum, then within about 50 years shallow soils of the Altcar complex in the areas mentioned above will have been converted to soils of the Downholland complex.

Within the Downholland complex, the presence of patches of Downholland Silt at the surface produces cultivation difficulties particularly in the soils of the first group, because the fine-textured material hardens on drying and it is difficult to obtain satisfactory surface structures and fine tilths for seed beds. Although the surface horizons are readily permeable, the presence of a permanent groundwater table restricts the downward movement of water through the lower layers. Lateral water movement in the Downholland complex is also restricted by the lack of sufficient fall in areas rarely more than 15 ft. above sea-level. Because of this, pumping is necessary in the Great Altcar district and a similar installation would undoubtedly benefit the drainage of the soils on Lytham Moss and around Great Marton.

A further problem of drainage is the rapidity with which tile drains become choked with silt and fine sand. The occurrence of Bg and Cg horizons with laminations of fine sand and silt is the basic cause and in some localities the effective life of tile drainage schemes may be as little as ten years.

The Downholland complex around Great Altcar is mainly devoted to the production of cereals and potatoes. Short-term leys provide both hay, often as a cash crop, and the necessary break in the essentially arable rotation. This district contrasts strongly with the Great Marton and Lytham Moss areas of the Downholland complex, the former of which is renowned for its intensive horticulture and flourishing glasshouse industry, winter lettuce, tomatoes, and chrysanthemums being the principal crops grown. Although there is also considerable cash cropping on the field scale on Lytham Moss this is normally supplemented by dairying and sheep enterprises. Cropping on the Downholland complex is extremely variable at the present time but it is possible that this flexibility will decrease as the valuable peat surface soils gradually waste away.

SOILS FROM ESTUARINE ALLUVIUM

During the 19th century considerable areas of alluvium in the Ribble estuary were enclosed by embankments and the land reclaimed for agriculture (*Plate IIIb*). The soils have been grouped as the Hesketh complex and sub-divided into three mapping units:—soils on active estuarine alluvium, soils on recent estuarine alluvium and a shallow phase overlying peat. The complex occupies 3,330 acres on the Southport sheet but is not represented on the Formby sheet.

HESKETH COMPLEX

Active estuarine alluvium is confined to Marshside, Crossens and Banks Out Marshes which form the south-west continuation of Hesketh Out Marsh where this complex was first recognized (Crompton, 1966). The soil pattern on this flat expanse of unenclosed marsh, with its many small pools and gullies, reflects the progress of deposition with coarser-textured surface soils in close proximity to the sea and soils of increasingly finer texture further inland. The soils are young and show little horizon development attributable to pedogenesis although textures throughout the profiles are very variable. In general, the thickness of the surface accumulation of fine-textured material varies from little or none at the edge of the salt-marsh, to about 2 ft. adjacent to the embankments. A typical profile (La 125) has a surface Ag horizon of dark grey or dull grey-brown, strongly rust mottled silty clay, with weakly developed sub-angular blocky or blocky structures and with occasional laminae of light grey or brownish grey fine sand and very dark grey silt with a high amount of organic matter. The Ag horizon is sharply distinguished from the underlying B/Cg horizon which is normally strongly laminated with bands of fine sand and silt. The strong rusty mottling distinguishes it from the Cg horizon in which mottles are few and the colour is grey to dark grey. These features, which occur throughout all profiles together with prominent rust mottles and black organic staining above the zone of permanent waterlogging, are produced by a combination of tidal flooding and ground-water table fluctuations. Calcium-carbonate contents of up to 10 per cent. are common, the carbonate being present as both large and finely comminuted fragments of shells. In the Ag horizon pH values of 7·0 to 7·5 are common and values of 8·0 to 8·5 are found in the B/Cg and Cg horizons and the profile is base saturated throughout.

The natural vegetation is dominated by sea poa (*Puccinellia maritima*) and creeping fescue. Sea poa occurs more commonly on the fine-textured material where water tends to stand at or near the surface for long periods after tidal flooding whilst creeping fescue dominates the coarse-textured soils through which flood water more readily percolates. On some of the drier sites common bent-grass is found in association with creeping fescue. Additional species in the sea poa community are sea arrow-grass (*Triglochin maritima*), glasswort (*Salicornia herbacea*) and scurvy-grass (*Cochlearia officinalis*), and in the fescue community, sea milkwort (*Glaux maritima*), thrift (*Armeria maritima*), sand spurrey (*Spergularia marginata*), sea aster (*Aster tripolium*), herbaceous seablight (*Suaeda maritima*) and sea plantain (*Plantago maritima*). Along the banks of the tidal channels sea purslane (*Halimione portulacoides*) and common beet (*Beta vulgaris*) are locally abundant.

The land is at present only used for rough grazing by cattle, but much is now in an ideal condition for reclamation from the sea because only thin surface accumulations of fine-textured material cover the coarser-textured subsoil (profile SD 32/9035, *Plate Vd*). With judicious cultivation the surface deposits could be mixed to form a soil of desirable texture. The longer reclamation is delayed the thicker the surface deposit of silty clay will become and eventually heavy machinery will be needed to incorporate it with the underlying coarser-textured material to form suitable arable soils. Such areas of fine-textured soils could, however, be maintained in excellent pasture.

The cultivated soils within the embankments total 1,590 acres occurring immediately inland from the Saltings from which they are separated by earth embankments. The soils are now completely protected from tidal flooding and are drained by systems of tile drains and a rectangular network of open ditches which empty through sluice gates into the Ribble estuary.

As on the Out Marshes, the soil pattern within each enclosed area is closely related to the distance from the inland or seaward embankments and is reflected in the presence of coarser-textured surface soils on the seaward side and finer-textured soils inland. The eastern boundary of the Hesketh complex is the former cliff-line cut in the boulder clay—the Hillhouse Coastline—clearly apparent on the southern edge of Banks Marsh and closely followed by the Banks–Hesketh Bank road.

The surface soil on the landward side of each enclosed area contains between 35 and 45 per cent. clay and there is a progressive increase in the amount of fine sand and silt towards the sea. This surface accumulation of fine-textured material is often more than 3 ft. thick adjacent to the Hillhouse Coastline where the profile, developed from very dark grey, silty clay or silty clay loam, has moderately developed, medium sub-angular blocky structures in the A horizon that overlies B/Cg and Cg horizons with strongly developed, coarse prismatic structures. The profile is intensely mottled above the zone of permanent water-logging largely due to the presence of many concretions of iron and manganese compounds.

Elsewhere, the most commonly occurring soil has a surface accumulation from 6 to 12 in. thick of fine texture which, when cultivated and mixed with sub-surface material, produces surface textures ranging from loam to silty loam with moderately developed coarse granular and medium sub-angular blocky structures. The B/Cg horizon is composed of laminae of silt and fine sand with weakly developed angular blocky structures. It is normally greyish brown to brownish grey in colour. Rust mottles are common in the upper parts of the Cg horizon but are almost non-existent below in the grey or greyish brown laminated silt and fine sand. The profile (La 107) described below illustrates the heterogeniety of the deposits in that the layer between 19 and 26 in. is almost wholly sand compared with the silty layers above and below it.

Farther inland the alluvium becomes thinner until peat is encountered within 3 ft. of the surface (profile La 111). A shallow phase of the Hesketh complex overlying peat has, therefore, been separated and occupies 560 acres on the Southport sheet east of Lytham St. Anne's, around Banks and north-east of Southport.

Most of the surface soils are of silt loam or fine sandy loam texture and silty clay surface soils are rare. The granular and sub-angular blocky structures are normally only moderately developed and problems of surface capping in the spring are a direct result of the poor aggregation resulting from the low contents of clay and organic matter. Structures in the underlying B/Cg horizon are less well developed and often the horizon consists of loose fine sand, greyish brown in colour with prominent rust mottles. It overlies a grey or dark grey Cg horizon with distinct strong brown mottles and staining on structure faces which, in turn, is sharply differentiated from the underlying peat.

Descriptions of representative profiles

PROFILE NO.: La 125 from the Saltings in the Hesketh complex; (analysis, p. 90).
Location: Banks (grid ref. SD 404239).
Relief: estuarine flat—Saltings.
Altitude: 3 ft. O.D.
Parent Material: active estuarine alluvium.
Land Use: rough grazing.
Horizons:

in.	
0–14 Ag	Dark grey (5 Y 4/1) silty clay with light brownish grey (2·5 Y 6/2) laminae of very fine sand; stoneless; weakly developed medium blocky to platy structure; sticky and plastic; abundant fine fibrous roots both living and dead with distinct strong brown stainings; distribution of the organic matter shows cycles of vegetation and silt deposition; sharp, undulating boundary.
14–21 B/Cg	Laminations of light brownish grey (2·5 Y 6/2) fine sand and dark grey (10 YR 4/1) silt loam; many prominent dark reddish brown (5 YR 3/4) and few reddish black (10 R 2/1) mottles; stoneless; moderate organic-matter content mainly associated with the silt loam laminae, fine and small dead roots common; few small shells; calcareous; sharp, even boundary.
21–42 Cg	Dark grey (5 Y 4/1) silt loam with laminae of greyish brown (2·5 Y 5/2) fine sand; occasional prominent dark reddish brown (5 YR 3/4) mottles; stoneless; moderate organic-matter content mainly associated with the silt loam laminae, few old fine roots; occasional small shells; calcareous; water-table at 42 in. May 13th 1959.

PROFILE NO.: SD 32/9035 from the Saltings in the Hesketh complex.
Location: Banks (grid ref. SD 390235).
Relief: estuarine flat.
Altitude: 3 ft. O.D.
Parent Material: active estuarine alluvium.
Land Use: rough grazing.
Horizon:

in.	
0–4 Ag	Dark greyish brown (2·5 Y 4/2) silty clay; stoneless; laminated; sticky and plastic; abundant fine fibrous roots; calcareous; sharp, even boundary.
4–12 B/Cg	Dark greyish brown (2·5 Y 4/2) bands of fine sand with bands of brown (10 YR 5/3) silt loam; many distinct dark reddish brown (5 YR 3/4) mottles between sand and silt bands; stoneless; strongly developed laminations; few fine fibrous roots; calcareous; merging, even boundary.
12–32 Cg1	Dark grey (5 Y 4/1) silt loam with greyish brown (2·5 Y 5/2) fine sand bands; occasional distinct dark reddish brown (2·5 YR 3/4) staining on old root channels; strongly developed laminations; calcareous; merging, even boundary.
32+ Cg2	Yellowish brown (10 YR 5/4) fine sand with brown (10 YR 4/3) silt loam bands; strongly developed laminations; occasional faint dark reddish brown (2·5 YR 3/4) and grey mottles associated with the sand bands; occasional large shell fragments; calcareous.

PROFILE NO.: La 107 from the Hesketh complex; (analysis, p. 90).
Location: Banks Marsh (grid ref. SD 388221).
Relief: flat estuarine plain.
Altitude: 5 ft. O.D.
Parent Material: recent estuarine alluvium.
Land Use: ley grassland.

Horizons:
in.

0–12   Dark greyish brown (10 YR 4/2) stoneless silt loam; moderately developed
A   fine to medium sub-angular blocky and granular structures; friable;
        moderate organic-matter content, abundant fine and small fibrous roots;
        occasional earthworms; sharp, even boundary.

12–19   Greyish brown (10 YR 5/2) stoneless loam; weakly platy; low organic-
B/C   matter content; slightly firm; numerous small shell fragments; few old
        roots and occasional old worm channels; sharp, even boundary.

19–26   Yellowish brown (10 YR 5/4) stoneless sand with many prominent reddish
Cg1   brown (5 YR 4/4) mottles; low organic-matter content; frequent shells and
        shell fragments; dark reddish brown (5 YR 3/4) staining at base of horizon
        with slight cementation; sharp, even boundary.

26+   Greyish brown (2·5 Y 5/2) fine sandy loam with very few reddish brown
Cg2   (5 YR 4/4) mottles; stoneless; laminae of fine sand and silt; slightly firm;
        low organic-matter content; water-table at 34 in. March 26th 1959.

PROFILE NO.: La 111 from the Hesketh complex, shallow phase (analysis, p. 90).
Location: Banks Marsh (grid ref. SD 379211).
Relief: estuarine flat.
Altitude: 5 ft. O.D.
Parent Material: recent estuarine alluvium.
Land Use: ley grassland.
Horizons:
in.

0–9   Very dark greyish brown (10 YR 3/2) stoneless loam with few faint brown-
Ap   ish yellow (10 YR 6/8) mottles associated with old roots; moderately
        developed fine and medium sub-angular blocky and granular structures;
        friable; moderate organic-matter content, abundant fine fibrous roots;
        occasional earthworms; occasional shells and shell fragments; sharp,
        undulating boundary.

9–15   Light yellowish brown (10 YR 6/4) stoneless loamy sand with many
B/Cg   distinct strong brown (7·5 YR 5/6) mottles; weakly developed medium
        blocky structure; very friable; low organic-matter content, mainly associ-
        ated with old earthworm channels, few fine fibrous roots; occasional
        earthworms; occasional shell fragments; merging, irregular boundary.

15–25   Brown (10 YR 5/3) loamy sand with many prominent reddish brown
Cg1   (5 YR 5/3) mottles; some gravel and small rounded stones; weakly devel-
        oped medium blocky structure; very friable; low organic-matter content,
        few small dead roots; occasional shell fragments; sharp, even boundary.

25–33   Dark grey (2·5 YR 4/0) stoneless loam with many distinct strong brown
Cg2   (7·5 YR 5/8) mottles and staining on structure faces; moderately developed
        large blocky structure; firm; moderate organic-matter content, small and
        medium dead roots common; occasional shell fragments; sharp, even
        boundary.

33–60   Dark yellowish brown (10 YR 4/4) fibrous fen peat with bands of black
        (2·5 Y 2/0) amorphous peat; sharp, even boundary.

60+   Dark grey (2·5 YR 4/0) stoneless silt loam; plastic; high organic-matter
        content.

The calcareous nature of the soils of the complex results from the presence
of shells and finely comminuted shell fragments. The surface soils are generally
highly calcareous so that pH values regularly exceed 7·0 although the oldest
deposits east of Churchtown and Banks and north of Lytham St. Anne's are
decalcified to various depths.

The high ground-water table results in poor subsoil drainage but is generally not detrimental to the intensive cropping practiced on these soils. Normally the surface horizons are very permeable and drain freely but the soils with a considerable thickness of silty clay or clay loam at the surface are only slowly permeable and water frequently stands at the surface after heavy rain. Much of the land is drained by systems of tile drains and open ditches, the water passing through sluice gates into the Ribble estuary. A common problem of tile drains in these soils with high contents of silt and fine sand is the rapidity with which they become blocked with silt.

In the surface soils with low percentages of clay, the surface capping of fine sand and silt experienced during dry springs results in the patchy emergence of seedlings. The problem is associated with weak structure in soils with low amounts of organic matter and could, to some extent, be remedied by the more widespread use of farmyard manure which would assist in the formation of stable aggregates.

Most of the land occupied by the cultivated phase of the Hesketh complex is devoted to intensive arable farming, dominated by brassicas and cereals between Banks and Churchtown. North of the Ribble, however, dairying with arable enterprises is the rule so that much of the complex north of Lytham St. Anne's is under grassland.

SOILS FROM RIVERINE ALLUVIUM

ALT COMPLEX

The watershed separating the Alt and Ditton brook is between Prescot and Huyton from whence the Alt flows north-west through Croxteth Park and first appears on the Formby sheet near Aintree. From Aintree to Carr Houses the Alt flows north-west across a broad valley floor, where its meanders are now embanked to prevent flooding. South of Great Altcar the valley opens out into an extensive flood plain across which the river flows west before turning south to enter the sea near Hightown.

Deep deposits of alluvium occur south of Great Altcar stretching west to Raven Meols. This broad delta-shaped area covers 1,340 acres and may be up to a mile wide at approximately 15 ft. O.D., with the river flowing close to the southern edge of the deposit. Flooding is still a problem and although the river is embanked a pumping station is needed to achieve a satisfactory flow of water from this low-lying district. The landscape is one of few hedges and trees with a network of open ditches and sluices separating rectangular fields.

The alluvium varies in texture from loam to silty clay often with silt and fine sand laminations. It also varies in thickness and, south-east of Great Altcar, overlies peat or sand and gravel. The soils have therefore been mapped as the Alt complex in which phases are separated where peat or sand and gravel underlies the alluvium.

Surface soils vary in texture from sandy loam to clay loam and have well developed granular and sub-angular blocky structures. These are sharply separated at plough depth from the underlying Bg horizon of grey, strongly rust mottled, silty clay or sandy clay loam with moderately developed blocky and fine prismatic structures. At approximately 18 in. from the surface the blocky structures are less well developed and laminations of silt and fine sand are clearly evident. The Cg horizon consists of laminations of grey silty clay and light grey fine sand in which the intensity of rust mottles decreases with depth.

The textures of surface soils adjacent to the Formby series between Raven Meols and Little Altcar are coarser as a result of the occasional deposition of blown sand and range from sandy loam to loam. Adjacent to the river and drainage channels, where silty clay, obtained from dredging, has been spread on the land, the textures of the surface soils are finer.

The soils are often only of low permeability and this defect is accompanied by the presence of a fluctuating ground-water table. The poor natural drainage, however, has been improved by open ditches and tile drainage schemes that have effected a speedier removal of rain water and prevent the ground-water from rising too close to the surface so that poor drainage is not now a factor limiting plant growth.

The organic-matter content of the surface soil is generally low and is not increased greatly in a district of intensive arable cultivation where little farmyard manure is applied. The generally fine texture of the surface soil makes autumn ploughing a necessity so that the winter frost can produce the tilth required for cereal and root crops. The soils have moderate cation-exchange capacities, are generally nearly base saturated and are neutral to slightly acid in reaction with pH values at the surface ranging between 6·0 and 7·0; calcium carbonate may be about 2 per cent. in the lower horizons. The soils, therefore, contrast strongly with those of the Hesketh complex which are usually quite calcareous throughout the profile.

From near the pumping station north of Carr Houses upstream to Sefton Meadows, the Alt alluvium overlies peat, as in Profile La 102 and this shallow phase of the complex is separated where peat occurs within 3 ft. of the surface. Covering 720 acres, it forms a narrow strip of land rarely more than $\frac{1}{4}$ mile wide with the embanked river flowing down the middle. The thickness of the alluvium decreases with distance from the river so that peat eventually occurs at the surface.

The surface soil is dark grey, strongly rust mottled, and often humose, loam or silt loam with moderately developed granular structures. It is sharply separated from the grey to greyish brown, rust mottled, loam or silty clay loam Bg horizon having moderately developed blocky structures. This merges into a Cg horizon of grey, faintly rust mottled, clay or silty clay loam with coarse blocky structures where the alluvium is more than 18 in. thick. Where the alluvium is less than 18 in. thick the Bg horizon rests directly on peat.

The organic-matter content of the surface varies from 12 to 20 per cent.—the higher amounts being common where the alluvium is thinnest. The soils are slightly acid with pH values ranging from 5·5 to 6·0 and the high base-exchange capacities are a direct result of the high organic-matter contents.

Periodic flooding is a problem in this area due to a combination of the high ground-water table and water standing on the surface after heavy rain. The level of the area known as Sefton Meadows, however, has now been raised by 12–15 ft. by dumping town waste, and the topsoil, removed before dumping began, has been replaced on the compacted refuse and the "meadows" have been reseeded for sheep and cattle grazing.

South-east of Sefton Meadows and as far as Aintree the alluvium overlies sand and gravel and 700 acres are mapped as a shallow phase of the complex (profile La 105). Between Sefton Meadows and the A59 road south of Maghull the river is embanked but south-east of the road it is cutting into the underlying boulder clay. Where the alluvium thins out, sand and gravel appear at the surface and ground-water gley soils of the Rufford series are well developed, particularly south-west of Cascough Lane.

Where periodic flooding occurs the land is under permanent grass but south-east of the A59 intensive arable cropping is general with potatoes, brassicas and cereals dominant.

Descriptions of representative profiles

PROFILE NO.: La 93 from the Alt complex; (analysis, p. 86).
Location: Altcar (grid ref. SD 314058).
Relief: flood plain of the Alt.
Altitude: 10 ft. O.D.
Parent Material: riverine alluvium.
Land Use: ley grassland.
Horizons:

in.

0–9 Ap — Very dark greyish brown (10 YR 3/2) stoneless loam; moderately developed medium sub-angular blocky and granular structures; firm; moderate organic-matter content, abundant fine and small fibrous roots; frequent earthworms; recently limed; sharp, even boundary.

9–17 Bg — Grey (5 Y 5/1) stoneless silty clay loam with many prominent yellowish red (5 YR 4/8) mottles throughout structural units and along old root channels; moderately developed small and medium prismatic structures, the faces of which are polished; firm; high organic-matter content associated with old root and earthworm channels, few fine living and dead fibrous roots; occasional earthworms; merging, irregular boundary.

17–25 B/Cg — Greyish brown (10 YR 5/2) silty clay loam with grey to light grey (10 YR 6/1) laminae of fine sand, strong brown (7·5 YR 5/6) mottles within structural units; laminated; firm; moderate organic-matter associated with old roots and earthworm channels, few fine living and dead roots; occasional earthworms; merging, irregular boundary.

25+ Cg — Greyish brown (10 YR 5/2) silty clay loam with grey to light grey (10 YR 6/1) fine sand laminae prominently mottled strong brown (7·5 YR 5/6); dark coloured staining mainly associated with old fibrous and woody roots; laminated structure.

PROFILE NO.: La 102 from the Alt complex, shallow phase; (analysis, p.86).
Location: Ince Blundell (grid ref. SD 338036).
Relief: flood plain of the Alt.
Altitude: 12 ft. O.D.
Parent Material: riverine alluvium.
Land Use: permanent grassland.
Horizons:

in.

0–2 A(g) — Dark greyish brown (10 YR 4/2) stoneless silt loam with many prominent yellowish red (5 YR 4/8) mottles mainly associated with dead roots; moderately developed fine and medium granular structures; friable; high organic-matter content, extremely abundant fine fibrous roots forming a mat; numerous earthworms; recently limed; sharp, irregular boundary.

2–5 Ag — Olive-grey (5 Y 4/2) stoneless clay loam with dark red (2·5 YR 3/6) staining on old roots; moderately developed small blocky structure; friable; high organic-matter content, abundant fine fibrous roots; numerous earthworms; sharp, irregular boundary.

5–9 Bg	Greyish brown (10 YR 5/2) stoneless silty clay loam with many dark reddish brown (2·5 YR 3/4) mottles associated with old roots; moderately developed fine sub-angular blocky and granular structures; friable; high organic-matter content, abundant fine fibrous roots; numerous earthworms; sharp, even boundary.
9–20	Black (5 YR 2/1) amorphous peat with few wood remains.
20+	Yellowish brown fibrous fen peat; water-table at 29 in. March 18th 1959.

PROFILE NO.: La 105 from the Alt complex, shallow phase; (analysis, p. 86).
Location: Maghull (grid ref. SD 361015).
Relief: flood plain of the Alt.
Altitude: 18 ft. O.D.
Parent Material: riverine alluvium.
Land Use: permanent grassland.
Horizons:

    in.

0–7 A	Very dark greyish brown (10 YR 3/2) sandy loam with some bleached sand grains; occasional rounded small stones and cinders; weakly developed medium sub-angular blocky and granular structures; friable; high organic-matter content, fine and small fibrous roots common; numerous earthworms; merging, even boundary.
7–14 B/C(g)	Dark brown (7·5 YR 4/2) sandy clay loam with few faint yellowish red mottles associated with old roots; occasional small rounded stones; weakly developed medium blocky and granular structures; friable; moderate organic-matter content, fine fibrous roots common; occasional earthworms; sharp, irregular boundary.
14–16 Cg1	Light brown (7·5 YR 6/4) sand with occasional small rounded stones; structureless; loose; low organic-matter content, but higher in old earthworm channels; merging, irregular boundary.
16–20 Cg2	Light grey (2·5 Y 7/2) sand with few distinct reddish yellow (5 YR 6/8) mottles; occasional small pockets of gravel; structureless; loose; low organic-matter content but higher in earthworm channels; sharp, irregular boundary.
20+	Light yellowish brown (10 YR 6/4) sand with few distinct yellowish red (5 YR 4/6) mottles and streaks; occasional small rounded stones; structureless; loose; water-table at 27 in. March 23rd 1959.

DOUGLAS COMPLEX

Narrow strips of fresh-water alluvium of mixed origin border streams throughout the area. They occupy 990 acres of which 670 acres occur on the Formby sheet. The main streams occur south of the Ribble and flow westward across the boulder clay and Shirdley Hill Sand in short narrow valleys with steep sides. The Sudell brook between Aughton and Hillhouse, the Chisnall brook between Barton and Haskayne and the stream between Brook House Farm and White House Farm, Halsall, are typical of these westward-flowing streams. The deposits of alluvium in the Black brook (between New House Farm and Sandy Brook Farm, Scarisbrick) and Sandy brook between Scarisbrick and Bescar Lane are often only thin and overlie peat. North of the Ribble, alluvium occurs as small patches around Westby Mills and on flat land between ridges of boulder clay in Ribby with Wrea.

The alluvium is often laminated and the profiles show little development other than that attributable to the effects of very poor drainage. Both site and profile drainage are invariably poor and the occurrence of the soils on sites liable to flooding and the presence of a fluctuating water-table makes artificial drainage difficult.

The soils have been grouped with the Douglas complex, first described farther east (Crompton, 1966). Surface soils are often humose and the loss on ignition attains 20 per cent. The soils are normally silt loam, clay loam or clay but are of coarser texture where material from the Shirdley Hill Sand has been incorporated.

The Bg and Cg horizons are predominantly grey in colour with frequent rusty mottlings. They are fine-textured and give rise to fine sub-angular blocky structures and are often underlain by peat adjacent to the Black brook and Sandy brook in the Scarisbrick district.

Most of the sites occupied by the Douglas complex are liable to flooding and consequently much of the land is permanent grassland.

Description of a representative profile

PROFILE NO.: La 124 from the Douglas complex; (analysis, p. 88).
Location: Hillhouse (grid ref. SD 355062).
Relief: flat river flood plain.
Altitude: 19 ft. O.D.
Parent Material: riverine alluvium.
Land Use: permanent grassland.
Horizons:

in.	
0–8 A	Very dark greyish brown (10 YR 3/2) stoneless clay; moderately developed fine to medium sub-angular blocky and granular structures; slightly firm; high organic-matter content, abundant fine fibrous roots; numerous earthworms; merging, undulating boundary.
8–15 B/Cg	Dark brown (7·5 YR 3/2) stoneless clay with a few strong brown (7·5 YR 5/6) soft concretions; moderately developed fine sub-angular blocky structure; firm; high organic-matter content, abundant fine and small fibrous roots; occasional earthworms; merging, even boundary.
15–22 Cg	Dark brown (7·5 YR 3/2) silty clay with few distinct strong brown (7·5 YR 5/6) mottles associated with old roots; moderately developed fine sub-angular blocky structure; firm; high organic-matter content, abundant fine fibrous roots; occasional earthworms; merging, even boundary.
22–27	Dark greyish brown (10 YR 4/2) silty clay with many distinct yellowish red (5 YR 4/8) mottles associated with fine, old root channels; stoneless; weakly developed medium sub-angular blocky structure; plastic; high organic-matter content, few fine fibrous roots; earthworms rare; sharp, even boundary.
27+	Very pale brown (10 YR 7/3) stoneless sand with few distinct reddish yellow (5 YR 6/8) mottles; structureless; loose; water-table at 32 in. May 7th 1959.

CHAPTER VI

Organic Soils

Peat may be defined in very broad terms as an accumulation of plant remains in varying stages of decomposition and formed under anaerobic conditions in stagnant or slowly flowing water. It is essentially the "parent material" for peat soils and the surface horizons, under the influence of soil-forming factors, constitute the solum.

It is estimated that about 13,800 acres of peat occur on the Southport and Formby sheets at altitudes ranging from about 3–25 ft. O.D. according to the most recent O.S. maps but shrinkage and wastage may have further lowered levels. These extensive tracts have been classified according to their mode of origin as intrazonal bog. All are basin peats originating in depressions formed behind sand spits, mudbanks or accumulations of blown sand on the coastal raised beaches. The environment, rich or moderately rich in nutrients, and the gradual infilling of the basins with vegetation resulted in the successive formation of reedswamp, fen and fen-carr peats to a stable stage of Low Moor. The type of peat accumulating at this stage was determined by the nutrient status and reaction of the ground-water and consequently the pattern of distribution varied according to local conditions. South of the Ribble on Halsall, Churchtown and Scarisbrick Mosses peat accumulation beyond the Low Moor stage took place. Growth became dependent solely upon rainfall and acid tolerant species were able to establish themselves to form an early stage of Raised Moss.

Two subdivisions of the peat have been distinguished on the basis of (a) botanical composition, according to the dominant peat-forming vegetation, (b) structure, whether fibrous, pseudo-fibrous or amorphous, and (c) the degree of decomposition or humification. The soils associated with these two groups have been mapped as the Altcar and Turbary Moor complexes.

Organo-mineral muds are confined within the boundary of Martin Mere which was a significant feature of the original mossland landscape but is now drained and reclaimed for agriculture. Its soils have been grouped into the Martin Mere complex (Crompton, 1966).

After the severe flooding which took place in 1954, when it was estimated that over 11,000 acres of agricultural land were affected and hundreds of acres of potatoes were lost, there was an overall feeling of insecurity among farmers, particularly those managing peat land. At the request of the Lancashire Rivers Board a field survey was carried out by the Soil Survey of England and Wales in conjunction with the National Agricultural Advisory Service and the Agricultural Land Service to obtain more precise information on the structure of the Mosses and the nature of the underlying mineral deposits. Borings were made along traverses across land mapped as peat. The traverse lines were set at $\frac{1}{3}$ of a mile apart and borings were taken at intervals of 440 yds. along them. Additional borings were made when features of particular interest were encountered. A

Hiller peat auger was used and samples were taken at intervals of 1 ft. at each site. By this means it was possible to note and tabulate changes in structure, to determine the thickness of the peat and also the nature of the underlying mineral formation. Some 500 borings along 41 traverse lines were taken and those applicable to the Southport and Formby sheets are shown in Fig. 7.

The thickness of the peat is extremely variable and underlying mineral deposits include reddish brown till, Shirdley Hill Sand and Downholland Silt. North of the Ribble the Mosses are underlain primarily by Downholland Silt but till is in evidence under shallow peat on the sides of the trough-like valleys.

To the south of the Ribble, till occurs under the Mosses around Banks and Shirdley Hill Sand underlies the peat adjacent to the Hillhouse Coastline and presumably represents the old beach. It grades westwards into Downholland Silt which underlies the peat deposits continuously towards the coast (Fig. 7).

Silt bands of variable texture (silts, fine sandy silts, silty fine sands), occur sandwiched in the peat south of Plex Moss and are particularly prominent on the western sides of Altcar and Downholland Mosses. The depth at which these bands occur varies considerably. On Altcar Moss they appear between 1 and 7 ft. but are most frequent between 1 and 3 ft. On Downholland and Plex Mosses the depth is usually between 4 and 6 ft. The existence of silt bands in close proximity to the surface will clearly affect future soil development for wastage of the peat will ultimately expose the silt with the formation of soils of the Downholland complex. In these areas it is likely that cultivation patterns will be affected and that additional drainage problems will arise. During the flooding in 1954 the localities in which silt bands occurred at shallow depth were particularly prone to serious waterlogging. The thickness of the silt bands is very variable, ranging from a few inches to several feet.

Appreciable quantities of blown sand are mixed in the surface horizons of the peat soils along the western boundary of the mosses, and also on the eastern portions of Plex, Downholland and Barton Mosses, where islands of Shirdley Hill Sand crop out.

All the peat deposits throughout the area have been reclaimed and are under agricultural management, except for small areas of raw moss confined to woodland but these have been disregarded on the map.

The profile of cultivated peat soils generally consists of Ap and C horizons. The cultivation layer is very dark brown to black in colour, with no recognizable remains, and weakly to moderately developed structures. It has a higher bulk density and specific gravity and increased ash content as compared with the C horizon into which it passes clearly and sharply but the moisture-holding capacity is much reduced (Table 11, p. 80).

Under cultivation, peat is lost by oxidation and occasionally by wind-blowing so that if the thickness of the ploughed layer is to be maintained a compensating amount of raw peat must be turned up annually and mixed into the Ap horizon.

ALTCAR COMPLEX

The Altcar complex, covering 4,580 acres on the Formby sheet and 4,190 acres on the Southport sheet, includes a variety of organic soils formed from reed-swamp, carr and fen-carr peats that had reached the Low Moor stage. North of the Ribble these peats are widely distributed but south of the river they are

6

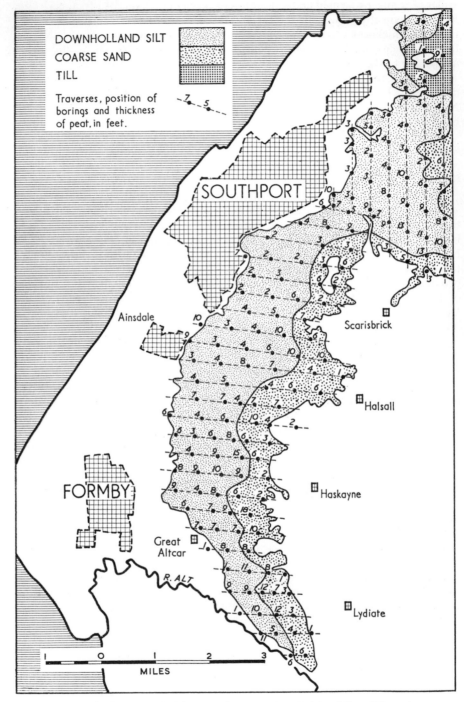

Fig. 7. Distribution and Thickness of Peat, and Underlying Mineral Deposits, south of the Ribble.

located in the extensive area of mossland running parallel to the coastline from Banks to Homer Green.

The vegetation forming reedswamp peat is of comparatively uniform botanical composition consisting almost entirely of *Phragmites communis* and *Carex* species. The peat varies from a few inches to several feet in thickness and overlies Downholland Silt or Shirdley Hill Sand. Where undisturbed by cultivation, it is fibrous or pseudo-fibrous, yellowish brown or brown in colour with flattened plant remains embedded in a loose rooty matrix. The upper layers are strongly to moderately acid in reaction with pH values between 4·0 and 4·8 but with increasing depth the values gradually increase and in the underlying mineral strata are of the order 6·0 to 7·0.

Under cultivation this type of peat produces a black or very dark brown, friable to slightly firm, amorphous peat soil (*Plate VIb*) which often contains mineral matter as a result of marling. Structures are generally weakly developed; medium sub-angular blocky and fine granular or crumb structures commonly occur but medium angular blocky structures that fall to fine granular under slight pressure are also found. The Ap horizon passes sharply at cultivation depth into reddish brown or brown, fibrous or pseudo-fibrous peat which becomes less humified and paler in colour with depth. In very wet weather the surface has a tendency to "pack" and infiltration into the surface is so reduced that ponding sometimes becomes extensive. During prolonged dry periods, however, the surface becomes hard, brittle and dusty and, in addition to the difficulty of re-wetting such dry peat, there is a danger of it blowing.

Over considerable areas originally covered by shallow reedswamp peat, wastage, due to cultivation, has resulted in the exposure of the underlying mineral strata which consist almost exclusively of Downholland Silt.

Carr peat occupies a limited zone mainly associated with the eastern periphery of most of the mosses and consists of tree and shrub remains mixed with the ground vegetation. The peat is very dark brown in colour and is generally well humified although the greater proportion consists of easily recognizable remains of wood. In the upper layers it is moderately acid in reaction with pH values of 5·0 to 5·5 but the values gradually increase to 6·0 to 6·5 at the base. The thickness of the peat ranges from 2 to 4 ft. and rarely exceeds this depth.

In typical profiles the Ap horizon consists of 7 to 12 in. of black or very dark brown loamy peat with a fine to medium sub-angular blocky and granular or crumb structure. This merges into very dark brown, relatively well humified peat (H 6–H 7) in which wood remains are plainly visible; noncoherent fine and medium angular blocky structures are strongly developed, the aggregates being slightly firm when moist but becoming hard and brittle when dry. Laminations and plant structures become more evident with depth and the remains of birch, alder, willow, oak, and occasional Scots pine, in varying stages of decomposition, are visible in the deposit.

The fen-carr peat comprises much of the peat filling the narrow valleys north of the Ribble whilst south of the river it is associated with reedswamp peat in local strips and pockets. In these areas a transition from reedswamp to fen and to fen-carr occurred as the surface dried out sufficiently for it to be colonized by terrestrial plants; this is strikingly revealed by studies of peat stratigraphy which also show that the thickness of fen-carr peat above the reedswamp peat is variable. The peat is of very mixed botanical composition with remains of cyperaceous and graminaceous plants and occasional soft, woody fragments of birch, alder and willow. It is fibrous or pseudo-fibrous, brown to dark brown in colour with a laminated structure that becomes more evident with depth. It invariably overlies fibrous reedswamp peat. Under cultivation the Ap horizon is black amorphous peat or loamy peat with weakly developed sub-angular blocky or soft crumb structures. It is friable and very porous but may become slightly compacted and the aggregates become firm towards the base of the horizon. There is a sharp and distinct change to fibrous or pseudo-fibrous peat at plough depth.

Descriptions of representative profiles

PROFILE NO.: SD 30/4745 from the Altcar complex.
Location: Altcar Moss (grid ref. SD 347045).
Altitude: 10 ft. O.D.
Parent Material: reedswamp peat.
Land Use: ley grassland.
Horizons:

in.		
0–10 Ap	Black (5 YR 2/1) loamy peat; stoneless; friable; weakly developed medium sub-angular blocky and granular structures; very porous; numerous fine and occasional large fissures; abundant fine and small fibrous and fleshy roots; occasional earthworms; sharp, even boundary.	
10–18 C1	Dark reddish brown (5 YR 2/2) fibrous reedswamp peat mainly composed of *Phragmites* and *Carex* spp.; relatively well humified (H5–H6); merging, even boundary.	
18–96 C2	Yellow-brown fibrous reedswamp peat with yellow plant remains in a dense rooty matrix; very slightly humified (H2); waterlogged, water-table standing at 31 in. May 5th 1963.	
96+	Blue-grey silty clay (Downholland Silt).	

PROFILE NO.: SD 30/3961 from the Altcar complex.
Location: Hillhouse (grid ref. SD 339061).
Altitude: 17 ft. O.D.
Parent Material: carr peat.
Land Use: ley grassland.
Horizons:

in.		
0–9 Ap	Black (10 YR 2/1) loamy peat; stoneless; weakly developed fine sub-angular blocky and granular structures; friable; very porous; abundant fine and small fibrous and fleshy roots; occasional earthworms; sharp, even boundary.	
9–16 C1	Very dark brown pseudo-fibrous carr peat; some soft wood remains; few distinct strong brown (7·5 YR 5/8) mottles associated with root channels and aggregate faces; well humified (H7–H8); strongly developed fine and medium angular blocky structures; abundant fine fissures; fine fleshy roots common decreasing to few at base of horizon; merging, even boundary.	
16–27 C2	Very dark brown fibrous carr peat; well humified (H5–H6); sharp, even boundary.	
27+	Very dark brown (10 YR 2/2) stoneless sand with prominent very dark grey (10 YR 3/1) mottles; structureless; abundant pores; the colour becomes progressively paler with depth to greyish brown (10 YR 4/2).	

PROFILE NO.: SD 30/4538 from the Altcar complex.
Location: Altcar (grid ref. SD 345038).
Altitude: 11 ft. O.D.

Parent Material: fen-carr peat.
Land Use: ley grassland.
Horizons:

in.

0–9 Ap	Black (5 YR 2/1) loamy peat; stoneless; weakly developed medium sub-angular blocky and granular structures; friable; very porous; numerous fine and occasional large fissures; abundant fine and small fibrous and fleshy roots; occasional earthworms; sharp, even boundary.
9–26 C1	Very dark brown (10 YR 2/2) fibrous fen-carr peat mainly composed of sedge and grass roots, rhizomes and leaf fragments, occasional soft wood remains; slightly compacted; slightly humified (H4–H5); sharp, even boundary.
26–60 C2	Yellowish brown fibrous reedswamp peat; very slightly humified (H2–H3); waterlogged.
60+	Blue-grey silty clay (Downholland Silt).

MARTIN MERE COMPLEX

The soils of this complex are confined within the boundary of the former tract of standing water known as Martin Mere. The lake was approximately 4 miles long and 2 miles wide, but, because it was situated in a flat area, with mossland to the north, west and south, its size varied considerably depending on the season of the year and climatic conditions. Old maps agree in showing three islands in the lake but differ as to their relative size and position. Berry House undoubtedly stands on one of the islands, formed by a hillock of boulder clay and, at the most, would have stood some 5 ft. above the highest water-level of the mere. It has not been possible to determine the position of the other two islands during recent work in the area.

In 1692 Thomas Fleetwood of Bank Hall obtained an Act of Parliament permitting him to drain the mere and in 1693 he employed as many as 2,000 workmen to cut a drainage channel, now known as The Sluice, to the sea at Crossens. Flooding was reduced by the installation of flood-gates, constructed in The Sluice near the sea, which automatically closed when the sea rose higher than the water in The Sluice and opened again when the tide fell. Periodic flooding, however, still occurred and the land was used only for summer grazing. It was not until 1784, after considerable modifications had been made to the drainage system, that a part of the mere was cultivated and gave high returns of oats and barley but by 1789 it was again flooded as both the Leeds–Liverpool Canal and the Douglas had burst their banks. Although the drainage system functioned satisfactorily it was decided to utilize the ground in future for grazing rather than arable cropping because of the danger of similar accidents occurring again. In 1849 steam pumps were erected at Crossens and gravity discharge was abandoned; the pumps were later modified to burn oil and in 1960 a new pumping station was built (*Plate IVb*). The water-table can now be regulated with considerable benefit to agriculture under a system of intensive arable cropping (Prus-Chacinski and Harris, 1963).

Only the western edge of the former lake occurs on the Southport sheet, some 2 miles north of Bescar and the soils of the Martin Mere complex cover about 90 acres. The soils are formed on silty dark brown or black amorphous deposits often with pronounced laminations of fine sand and silt. The bulk of the deposit is an organo-mineral lacustrine mud consisting of the products of decomposition of organic matter, precipitated in shallow water and intimately mixed with silt and fine sand. The deposit is of variable thickness, depths up to 9 ft. having been recorded, and overlies fen-carr or *Sphagnum–Eriophorum* peat. A thin band of carr peat, mainly of hazel remains in a matrix of black amorphous peat, is frequently encountered at approximately 3 ft., suggesting that at one time the lake dried sufficiently for terrestrial plants to colonize the area.

Typical profiles have an Ap horizon of dark brownish grey or black, humose silty loam or loamy peat up to 12 in. thick with moderately developed, medium, sub-angular blocky and granular structures. The pronounced loamy character of the surface horizon is the result of the gradual oxidation of the organic fraction during cultivation and the resulting increase in the amount of inorganic material, mainly silt and fine sand. Mechanical analyses of samples from the Ap horizon gave an average figure of 70 per cent. mineral matter and 30 per cent. organic matter whilst samples of the C horizon from a depth between 30 and 36 in. gave a mean value of 75 per cent. organic matter and 25 per cent. mineral matter. Beneath the Ap horizon there is a sharp change to black, silty, amorphous peat in which there may be discontinuous, very thin laminations and lenticles of bleached fine sand or grey silt. This merges, at variable depth, into fibrous fen-carr or *Sphagnum–Eriophorum* peat.

Description of a representative profile

PROFILE NO.: SD 31/9170 from the Martin Mere complex.
Location: Martin Mere (grid ref. SD 391170).
Altitude: 10 ft. O.D.
Parent Material: lacustrine organic mud.
Land Use: ley grassland.
Horizons:

	in.	
0–12	Ap	Black (10 YR 2/1) stoneless peaty loam; friable; moderately developed, medium sub-angular blocky and medium granular structures; abundant small fibrous roots; occasional earthworms; sharp, even boundary.
12–26	C1	Black (10 YR 2/1) silty amorphous peat with occasional laminations and lenticles of bleached sand and grey silt; stoneless; slightly sticky and plastic; few fine fibrous roots; merging, even boundary.
26–29	C2	Black (5 YR 2/1) silty amorphous peat with a few distinct strong brown (7·5 YR 5/6) ferruginous mottles associated with old root channels; stoneless; slightly sticky and slightly plastic; laminated; merging, even boundary.
29–72	C3	Very dark brown (10 YR 2/2) pseudo-fibrous fen-carr peat; relatively well humified (H6–H7); strongly laminated; waterlogged, water-table at 32 in. February 12th 1962.
72+		Blue-grey silty clay (Downholland Silt).

TURBARY MOOR COMPLEX

The Turbary Moor complex, developed on Basin Peat at the Early Raised Moss stage, covers 3,220 acres on the Formby sheet and 1,720 acres on the Southport sheet. The deposits, which overlie reedswamp or fen peat, mainly consist of the remains of *Sphagnum* and *Eriophorum* species, with variable amounts of *Calluna vulgaris*. The thickness of the *Sphagnum–Eriophorum* peat rarely exceeds 2 or 3 ft. and represents the peat formed after the surface layers of mesotrophic reedswamp or fen peat rose above the influence of ground-water and further accumulation occurred under ombrogenous conditions. This marked change in vegetational character indicates development from the Low Moor to the pre-Raised Moss stage.

The raw peat varies in colour from yellowish brown to dark reddish brown, it is invariably fibrous and plant remains are easily recognized (*Plate VIc*). The peat is generally fairly tough, porous, and non-plastic and when it is dried it usually becomes looser and more porous without a great deal of shrinkage. It is strongly acid in reaction with pH values between 3·5 and 4·5.

A typical profile under cultivation has an Ap horizon of very dark brown or black amorphous peat, the thickness of which depends on the depth of ploughing, with moderately developed sub-angular blocky and granular or crumb structures (*Plate VId*). It is very friable when moist and becomes soft when dry. There is a sharp junction with the fibrous or, occasionally, pseudo-fibrous peat.

Description of a representative profile

PROFILE NO.: SD 31/8360 from the Turbary Moor complex.
Location: Scarisbrick Moss (grid ref. SD 383160).
Altitude: 13 ft. O.D.
Parent Material: Sphagnum–Eriophorum peat.
Land Use: ley grassland.
Horizons:

in.

0–8 Ap	Black (5 YR 2/1) stoneless loamy peat; very friable; moderately developed fine sub-angular blocky and granular structures; very porous; permeable; abundant fine and small fibrous roots; occasional earthworms; many fragments of fibrous peat distributed throughout the horizon; sharp, even boundary at cultivation depth.
8–18 C1	Dark reddish brown (5 YR 3/2) fibrous *Sphagnum–Eriophorum–Calluna* peat; slightly humified (H3–H4); strongly laminated; few fine fibrous roots; merging, even boundary.
18–22 C2	Dark reddish brown (2·5 YR 3/4) pseudo-fibrous *Sphagnum–Eriophorum* peat; well humified (H7); slightly plastic; laminated; sharp, even boundary.
22–31 C3	Yellowish brown fibrous reedswamp peat mainly of *Phragmites* remains; slightly humified (H4); merging, even boundary.
31–84 C4	Yellowish brown fibrous reedswamp peat with yellow plant remains in a dense rooty matrix; very slightly humified (H2); waterlogged.
84+	Blue-grey silty clay (Downholland Silt).

One of the main problems associated with mossland is that of maintaining adequate drainage particularly in areas so near to sea-level; artificial water-courses need to be kept in order and, over considerable areas, pumping is necessary. The surface of mossland, which is subject to intensive cultivation and concentrated drainage schemes, is being lowered at the rate of approximately $\frac{1}{4}$ to $\frac{1}{2}$ in. per annum. Severe problems result from this wastage, for tile drainage systems become exposed and have to be regraded and relaid and exposed tree-stumps and trunks, known as "moss stocks", have to be removed.

To compare the physical properties of the cultivated soil with those of the parent material an investigation was made of two soils of the Altcar complex, formed on reedswamp and carr peat respectively, and of a soil of the Turbary Moor complex, developed from *Sphagnum* and *Eriophorum* species with some *Calluna*. A soil of the Martin Mere complex was also included. The figures in

Table 11 are the average of several samples taken from the Ap horizon at 2–6 in. and from the C horizon at 18–22 in.

TABLE 11

Physical Properties of Organic Soils

(calculated on a basis of oven-dry soil)

Soils from	Horizon	Bulk density gm./cc.	Total moisture-holding capacity %	Ash %
Altcar complex (on reedswamp peat)	Ap C	0·38 0·10	152 637	31·0 4·0
Altcar complex (on carr peat)	Ap C	0·51 0·15	133 605	43·8 10·9
Turbary Moor complex	Ap C	0·45 0·14	183 863	33·0 4·7
Martin Mere complex	Ap C	0·75 0·29	84 311	66·7 35·2

The bulk densities of the three kinds of peat in the C horizons are similar but the presence of mineral matter in the organic mud of the Martin Mere soil has doubled its density. The effect of the addition of mineral matter by marling and manuring and the oxidation resulting from cultivation is to raise the densities of the surface soils by a factor of three but all are very low compared with mineral soils. These changes in the surface conditions are reflected in the figures for the total moisture-holding capacity of the Ap horizons which show a fourfold decrease when compared with the C horizon. The *Sphagnum–Eriophorum* peat has the highest moisture-holding capacity; this is attributable to the presence of the bladder-like leaves of Sphagnum moss which absorb and retain moisture. Under cultivation the ash content of the Ap horizon is increased; the content of the C horizon of the Martin Mere soil is high and the Ap horizon has acquired characteristics of a peaty loam.

TABLE 12

Available Copper in Organic Soils

Soil from	Horizon	Available copper (p.p.m.)*			
Altcar complex (on reedswamp peat)	Ap C	47·9 3·8	15·7 1·3	12·1 6·8	8·8 7·4
Altcar complex (on carr peat)	Ap C	15·5 7·7	9·9 2·3	19·2 7·1	14·6 2·1
Turbary Moor complex	Ap C	25·2 1·1	22·0 4·2	29·1 4·6	24·3 2·3
Martin Mere complex	Ap C	12·7 1·8	11·7 1·2	11·4 9·4	14·0 5·7

* Estimated colorimetrically after extraction with E.D.T.A.

Determinations for available copper were carried out on several samples of the main peat types, four from the Ap horizon at 2–6 in. and four from the C horizon at 18–22 in. None of the available copper figures in the cultivation layer are sufficiently low for the possible occurrence of copper deficiency in crops and no instances of "reclamation disease" have been reported from the area. It has been suggested that industrial pollution is responsible for these relatively high copper contents.

Cultivated peat has a high base-exchange capacity and when nutrients are applied they are held in a form easily assimilated by plant roots. Peat soils suffer but little from drought owing to their high absorptive capacity for moisture and the readiness with which the moisture is available to plants. Peat land is easily cultivated and is a medium upon which a fine tilth is readily produced. Although not an early soil and being especially susceptible to late frosts, it can nevertheless be considered among the most productive in the country.

Most of the mossland is under intensive arable cultivation, but in some places where it is apparently not possible to maintain an adequate drainage system, arable land is reverting to mixed fen or open carr. Such fields may be dominated either by sweet vernal-grass, Yorkshire fog, rushes or by a variety of mixed fen or open fen-carr vegetation, representing different stages of reversion. Two sites were selected to describe an early and a late stage in the process.

In the field chosen to illustrate the early stage (grid ref. SD 321094) the sward is dominated by sweet vernal-grass but, locally, patches of common bent-grass, purple moor-grass (*Molinia caerulea*) or Yorkshire fog, may become dominant. Additional species recorded were: sorrel, pennywort, tormentil (*Potentilla erecta*), purple loosestrife (*Lythrum salicaria*), devil's-bit scabious (*Succisa pratensis*), fiorin, sheep's fescue, common sedge, soft rush (*Juncus effusus*), and many-headed woodrush (*Luzula multiflora*).

In the late stage of reversion (grid ref. SD 323095) to mixed fen the community is a mosaic of small patches each dominated by any of the following: common sedge, Yorkshire fog, meadow-sweet (*Filipendula ulmaria*), yellow flag (*Iris pseudacorus*), sweet vernal-grass and reed-grass (*Phalaris arundinacea*). The following additional species were recorded: marsh cinquefoil (*Potentilla palustris*), soft rush, common sedge, common bent-grass, fiorin, tufted vetch (*Vicia cracca*), common meadow rue (*Thalictrum flavum*), yellow rattle (*Rhinanthus minor*), silverweed (*Potentilla anserina*), marsh bedstraw, rosebay willow-herb (*Chamaenerion angustifolium*), lesser knapweed, pennywort, sorrel.

CHAPTER VII

Analytical Data

To confirm and supplement field observations and to assist in the characterization of mapping units, samples are taken from each horizon of representative profiles for analysis. In this survey determinations of particle-size distribution (mechanical analysis), pH, calcium carbonate (where present), loss on ignition, exchangeable cations and percentage base saturation were made on all samples.

In the following Table 13, the order of the mapping units is alphabetical. All percentages are calculated on the oven-dry weight of the material that passes through a 2 mm. sieve. Some of the analytical data has been introduced and commented upon at appropriate places in the earlier chapters.

Particle-size Distribution

Determinations of particle-size distribution were made on all samples primarily to check field assessment of texture class. In the profile descriptions the textural class names are those derived from the mechanical analyses.

For surface horizons, and lower horizons of some profiles the results include percentages of clay (e.s.d. $< 2 \mu$), U.S.D.A. silt (e.s.d. $2–50 \mu$), fine sand (e.s.d. $50–200 \mu$) and coarse sand (e.s.d. $200–2,000 \mu$). Clay and silt were determined by the pipette method after treatment with hydrogen peroxide and dispersion with Calgon (sodium hexametaphosphate); the sand fractions were determined by the use of appropriate B.S. sieves. For the remaining sub-surface samples, clay and silt only were determined by the hydrometer method without removing the organic matter.

Besides providing a quantitative basis for textural classification, mechanical analyses supplement field observations regarding the origin and uniformity of the soil-forming materials and aid the designation of horizons. In identifying horizons of differing origin, emphasis is placed on the relative proportions of the sand and silt fractions, as these, together with stones, constitute the immobile "skeleton" of the soil; vertical changes in clay content may arise through translocation and weathering, as well as from variations in the conditions of deposition.

In the Southport and Formby districts almost all differences in textural classes are primarily the result of striking differences in parent materials. Textures range from sand to loamy sand on outcrops of Bunter and Keuper sandstones, on dune sand, glacial sand and gravel, and Shirdley Hill Sand; from silt loam to silty clay on active and recent alluvium and from sandy loam to clay loam on till.

Loss on Ignition

The loss on ignition provides a rough guide to the amount of organic matter in soils but the figure includes the loss of water forming part of the constitution of clay minerals, and that resulting from the ignition of elementary carbon and in calcareous soils, the loss of carbon dioxide from the calcium carbonate. A correction, where necessary, has been applied for the latter. For most soils an approximation to the organic-matter content can be obtained by subtracting $\frac{1}{10}$th of the percentage of clay from the percentage loss on ignition.

The range of loss on ignition in the surface soils is from 3 per cent. in the shallow phase of the Formby series on blown sand to 25 per cent. in the peaty phase of the Downholland complex on alluvium. The amount of organic matter usually decreases gradually with depth but in soils such as those of the Crannymoor series there is an increase at the Bh or Bhfe horizon.

Calcium Carbonate

Amounts of carbon dioxide evolved from calcareous samples on treatment with acid were determined volumetrically and the results expressed as percentages of calcium carbonate. Few of the soil profiles described have any carbonate in the upper layers, the exceptions being associated with alluvial deposits, dune sand or soils that have been recently limed. The lowest horizons of all soil profiles described on the reddish brown till contain up to 15 per cent. $CaCO_3$, much of which is of secondary origin; the upper layers of the soils developed in the till are non-calcareous.

The sand dunes along the coast between Southport and Hightown, and between South Shore, Blackpool and Lytham St. Anne's are also calcareous because of the presence of finely comminuted shells. Comminuted shell fragments also occur throughout soils derived from active and recent alluvium. Much of the Downholland Silt is also calcareous.

Soil Reaction (pH)

The pH of 1 : 2·5 soil suspensions was determined electrometrically in water and in M/100 calcium chloride solution. The values obtained by the latter method may be as much as one unit lower than in aqueous suspensions, but are thought to correspond more closely to the effective pH of the solution in immediate contact with the soil particles (Russell, 1961). They are also more reproducible and less affected by seasonal fluctuations in the concentration of the soil solution.

The reaction of a soil can be described in the following terms in relation to the pH values.

	pH (in water)
Strongly acid	<4·5
Moderately acid	4·5–5·5
Slightly acid	5·6–6·5
Neutral	6·6–7·5
Alkaline	>7·5

In the Southport and Formby districts neutral and alkaline surface soils occur on active and recent estuarine alluvium, on the coarser-textured phases of the Downholland Silt, and on recently stabilized sand dunes. Slightly acid soils are widespread on the brown earths and gley soils developed on till while moderately acid soils occur on sandstones, Shirdley Hill Sand, and other superficial sandy deposits. Practically all the slightly acid soils, however, are cultivated so that the tendency to surface acidity is corrected by additions of lime. Strongly acid soils are only associated with peat and occur particularly on raised moss mainly of *Sphagnum-Eriophowm* but the acidity of these soils is now corrected by liming and extreme acidity is no longer a limiting factor.

Exchangeable Cations and Percentage Base Saturation

Determinations of exchangeable cations were made only on the samples from non-calcareous horizons and the results are expressed in milli-equivalents per 100 gm. soil. The exchangeable metallic cations (exchangeable bases) calcium, magnesium, potassium and sodium were determined in a neutral normal ammonium acetate leachate, after evaporation to dryness and treatment with hydrogen peroxide to remove organic matter.

The capacity of a soil to retain cations in exchangeable form depends on the amount and kind of both organic and inorganic constituents, although the contribution of the inorganic material resides mainly in the clay fraction. As the organic component of the exchange complex usually has a higher exchange capacity, weight for weight, than the inorganic component, the total capacity of the soil commonly decreases below the surface, but may increase if the clay content increases.

For a broad classification of base-exchange capacity and the content of the individual cations the table below is a useful guide (Metson, 1956).

Base-exchange Capacity (m.e./100 gm.)

Very high	>40
High	25–40
Moderate	12–25
Low	6–12
Very low	<6

Exchangeable Bases (m.e./100 gm.)

	Ca	Mg	K	Na
Very high	>20	>8	>1·2	>2·0
High	10–20	3–8	0·8–1·2	0·7–2·0
Moderate	5–10	1–3	0·5–0·8	0·3–0·7
Low	2–5	0·3–1	0·3–0·5	0·1–0·3
Very low	<2	<0·3	<0·3	<0·1

In the soils examined the cation-exchange capacity varies from 1 to over 60 m.e./100 gm. The highest values of more than 50 m.e./100 gm. occur in the peats and peaty soils and values in subsoils developed on fine-textured till are only moderate to low in spite of their moderately high clay content. The lowest cation-exchange capacities occur in the strongly leached horizons of sandy soils, for example, of the Crannymoor and Sollom series on Shirdley Hill Sand in which values fall below 1 m.e./100 gm.

Almost all the soils on the calcareous alluvium are base-saturated throughout and very high amounts of exchangeable calcium account for most of the exchangeable metallic cations, and the percentage base saturation of the surface soils on these calcareous deposits rarely falls below 60–70 per cent.

It would be expected that the sub-surface horizons of strongly leached soils on sandstone, Shirdley Hill Sand, and fluvio-glacial sand and gravel would have low percentage base-saturation values. However, the widespread use of lime and fertilizers significantly increases the percentage base-saturation and figures of from 40 to 80 per cent. are common in these horizons with very low base-exchange capacities.

SUMMARY OF ANALYTICAL METHODS

1. Particle-size distribution: clay (e.s.d. $< 2\ \mu$) and silt (e.s.d. 2–50 μ) were deter mined, (a) by the pipette method after treatment with H_2O_2 and dispersion with Calgon and (b) by a modification of the hydrometer method (Bouyoucos, 1951), using Calgon as the dispersing agent. Appropriate B.S. sieves were used to separate the coarser fractions.
2. Calcium carbonate was determined by the use of Collins calcimeter.
3. pH measurements were made on 1 : 2·5 suspension of soil in water and in M/100 $CaCl_2$, using a glass electrode assembly.
4. Exchangeable cations were determined in a neutral normal ammonium acetate leachate, after evaporation to dryness and treatment with H_2O_2 to remove organic matter, by the Lundegårdh flame spectrographic method. The cation-exchange capacity was determined, after removal of excess ammonium acetate by treatment with alcohol, by leaching with normal sodium chloride and estimating ammonium in the leachate, using the Markham micro-distillation apparatus.

TABLE 13

Analytical Data for Mapping Units

(Arranged alphabetically)

Profile No.	Horizon	Depth in.	Sand 200μ–2 mm.	Sand 50μ–200μ	Silt 2μ–50μ	Clay <2μ	Loss on Ignition	$CaCO_3$ %	pH H_2O 1:2.5	pH $M/100$ $CaCl_2$	Ca	Mg	K	Na	Cation Exchange Capacity m.e./100 gm.	Percentage Base-saturation
Alt Complex																
La 93 (p. 69)	Ap	0–9	1	22	49	27	6·7		6·9	6·4	14·4	0·8	0·2	0·2	17·4	99
	Bg	9–17	5	7	55	38	8·9		6·5	6·0	9·9	1·6	0·2	0·3	11·2	98
	B/Cg	17–25			51	39	3·8	0·1	6·7	6·2	8·4	3·6	0·2	0·3	12·4	Sat.
	Cg	25+			51	34	3·7	1·8	7·5	6·9						
La 102 (p. 69)	A(g)	0–2	6	12	53	26	16·0		6·3	5·8	19·0	0·6	0·1	0·4	26·6	76
	Ag	2–5	6	14	47	30	13·6		5·6	5·0	10·0	0·3		0·2	23·6	44
	Bg	5–9	4	11	51	34	13·9		5·0	4·3	4·7	0·4	0·1	0·1	26·2	20
		9–20					76·8		4·6	4·0						
		20+					87·9		3·2	3·1						
La 105 (p. 70)	A	0–7	39	21	18	20	11·7	0·3	6·7	6·2	14·1	0·8	0·1	0·2	16·9	89
	B/C(g)	7–14	23	22	24	29	8·8	0·3	6·9	6·5	15·0	0·9	0·1	0·2	17·5	92
	Cg1	14–16			5	<1	0·3	0·3	7·3	6·5						
		16–20			<1	<1	0·3	0·2	7·4	6·6	0·6	0·1			0·8	88
	Cg2	20+			<1	<1			6·9	6·2						
Astley Hall Series																
La 103 (p. 36)	Ap	0–10			17	11	4·7		5·8	4·9	4·5	1·0	0·1	0·1	8·1	70
	B	10–22			12	12	2·1		6·2	5·4	4·4	0·4		0·1	5·7	86
	B(g)	22–28			12	12	2·3		6·3	5·6	4·4	0·4		0·1	6·2	79
	Cg	28+			30	35	3·9		6·5	6·0	9·3	1·1	0·1	0·2	8·0	Sat.

TABLE 13 (continued)

Profile No.	Horizon	Depth in.	Particle Size Distribution (per cent.)				Loss on Ignition	CaCO₃ %	pH		Exchangeable Cations m.e./100 gm.				Cation Exchange Capacity m.e./100 gm.	Percentage Base-saturation
			Sand 200μ–2 mm	Sand 50μ–200μ	Silt 2μ–50μ	Clay <2μ			H_2O 1:2·5	$M/100$ $CaCl_2$	Ca	Mg	K	Na		
Bridgnorth Series																
La 120 (p. 28)	A	0–9	47	25	14	12	5·8		4·8	4·1	1·3	0·1	0·1		9·0	17
	B1	9–16			8	13	2·6		4·7	4·0	0·6		0·1		6·6	12
	B2	16–27			10	11	2·2		5·8	4·8	3·0	0·2		0·1	6·6	50
Clifton Series																
La 99 (p. 52)	Ap(g)	0–6	30	30	23	14	7·6		6·2	5·4	6·8	0·7	0·1	0·2	9·1	85
	Bg or Ebg	6–10			24	17	3·0		6·6	5·8	8·7	0·6	0·1	0·2	13·2	73
	Bt(g)	10–12			27	38	4·2		6·6	6·1	6·7	1·3	0·1	0·2	12·2	68
	C(g)	12–32			30	41	3·9	0·2	7·3	6·7						
	C(g)ca	32–36			33	37	3·2	8·9	8·2	7·7						
Clive Series																
La 129 (p. 30)	A	0–8	41	27	17	14	6·0		6·8	6·2	10·5	0·3	0·1	0·1	10·3	Sat.
	B	8–21			9	16	2·6		6·6	5·8	5·0	0·4	0·3	0·1	7·3	79
Cottam Series																
La 108 (p. 54)	A(g)	0–7	10	29	36	23	9·9		5·4	4·7	7·6	0·6	0·1	0·2	16·4	52
	A(g) or Eb(g)	7–22			40	23	4·8		5·5	4·9	5·0	0·9	0·1	0·1	11·1	55
	Bt(g)	22–32			30	40	4·9		5·9	5·3	6·8	2·1	0·1	0·2	12·6	73
	C(g)	32–48			33	41	3·8	4·6	8·2	7·2						
	C(g)ca	48+			34	51	3·2	15·2	8·3	7·8						

TABLE 13 (continued)

Profile No.	Horizon	Depth in.	Sand 200μ–2mm	Sand 50μ–200μ	Silt 2μ–50μ	Clay <2μ	Loss on Ignition	CaCO₃ %	pH H₂O 1:2.5	pH CaCl₂ M/100	Ca	Mg	K	Na	Cation Exchange Capacity m.e./100 gm.	Percentage Base-saturation
Crannymoor Series																
La 90 (p. 30)	A1	0–2	56	21	12	8	10·9		7·4	7·0	9·7	0·2		0·2	21·2	50
	A2	2–9	60	23	10	6	8·4		7·0	6·6	3·8	0·1		0·1	4·6	87
	Bhfe	9–10	53	20	12	13	8·9		6·0	5·2						
	B/C	10–12			5	7	2·2		6·2	5·6						
La 89 (p. 42)	Ap	0–6	78	21	4	3	5·5		5·7	5·0	4·3	0·2		0·1	8·0	58
	Ea	6–9	78	19	<1	<1	0·7		5·7	5·4	0·9	0·1			1·3	85
	Bh	9–10	83	15	<1	<1	2·0		5·9	5·7	3·7	0·1	0·1	0·1	4·9	82
	Bhfe1	10–18	86	13	<1	<1	1·6		5·9	5·5	1·8	0·1		0·1	3·3	58
	Bhfe2	18–27	79	20	<1	<1	1·0		5·8	5·6	1·2	0·1		0·1	1·9	74
	C(g)	27+			<1	<1	0·6		5·9	5·6	0·6	0·1		0·1	1·2	58
Douglas Complex																
La 124 (p. 71)	A	0–8	8	7	30	55	17·6		6·1	5·5						
	B/Cg	8–15	2	6	35	56	22·9		5·8	5·2						
	Cg	15–22	1	2	41	56	28·4		5·7	5·3						
		22–27	3	6	49	41	15·3		5·5	5·0						

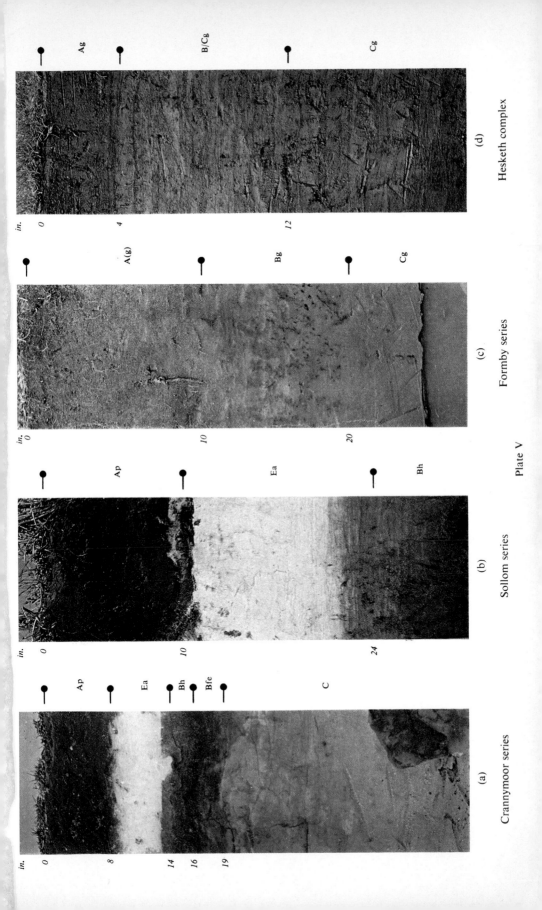

in.

(a) Crannymoor series

0
Ap
8
Ea
14
Bh
16
Bfe
19
C

(b) Sollom series

in.
0
Ap
10
Ea
24
Bh

(c) Formby series

in.
0
A(g)
10
Bg
20
Cg

(d) Hesketh complex

in.
0
Ag
4
B/Cg
12
Cg

Plate V

(a)
Downholland complex

(b)
Altcar complex

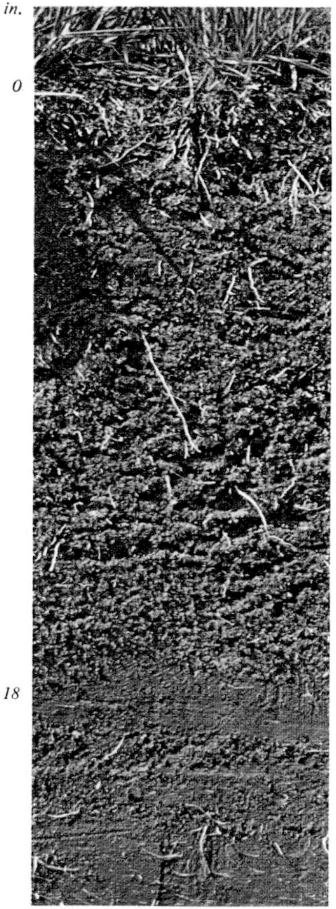

(c)
Turbary Moor complex,
unreclaimed

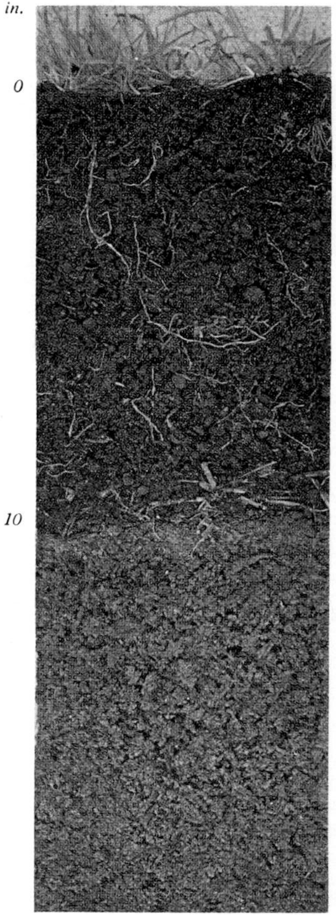

(d)
Turbary Moor complex,
under arable cultivation

Plate VI

TABLE 13 (continued)

Profile No.	Horizon	Depth in.	Sand 200 μ–2 mm.	Sand 50 μ–200 μ	Silt 2 μ–50 μ	Clay < 2 μ	Loss on Ignition	CaCO$_3$ %	pH H$_2$O 1:2.5	pH M/100 CaCl$_2$	Ca	Mg	K	Na	Cation Exchange Capacity m.e./100 gm.	Percentage Base-saturation
Downholland Complex																
La 95 (p. 60)	A	0–7	2	48	38	7	15·2		6·2	5·5	16·4	0·5	0·1	0·2	27·1	63
	Bg1	7–9			47	4	0·7	0·9	7·2	6·5						
	Bg2	9–33			51	6		5·5	8·5	7·8						
	Cg	33–37			54	5		9·2	8·7	8·0						
La 116 (p. 61)	Apg	0–7	15	21	40	23	18·2		6·7	6·1	25·5	0·9	0·1	0·2	30·1	89
	Bg	7–17			48	42	6·1		5·9	5·3	12·0	2·4	0·2	0·2	15·6	95
	Cg	17+			62	23	4·9		7·6	7·1						
La 118 (p. 61)	Apg	0–8	4	18	45	30	24·9		5·5	5·0	29·8	1·7	0·2	0·2	58·0	57
	C2g	8½+			57	31	5·2		5·8	5·3	7·8	1·9	0·2	0·1	13·3	72
Ellerbeck Series																
La 106 (p. 33)	Ap	0–11	48	22	15	12	10·4	0·4	7·2	6·6	5·0	0·2	0·1	0·1	9·3	58
	B1	11–15	48	55	13	13	5·5		6·2	5·4	2·5	0·2	0·1	0·1	6·3	44
	B2	15–20			11	7	3·8		6·3	5·3	2·3	0·3		0·1	5·9	46
	C1	20–27			15	9	3·2		7·4	6·6						
	C2	27+			27	37	3·6									

7

TABLE 13 (continued)

Profile No.	Horizon	Depth in.	Sand 200 μ–2 mm	Sand 50 μ–200 μ	Silt 2 μ–50 μ	Clay < 2 μ	Loss on Ignition	CaCO₃ %	pH H₂O 1:2.5	pH M/100 CaCl₂	Ca	Mg	K	Na	Cation Exchange Capacity m.e./100 gm.	Percentage Base-saturation
Formby Series																
La 92 (p. 46)	A	0–1½	61	32	4	2	12.5		4.5	3.6	0.1				1.0	1
	A(g)	1½–5½			4	<1	2.3		4.5	3.9	0.2	0.1			2.8	7
	Bg1	5½–8½			5	<1	1.6		4.9	4.1	0.4	0.1			2.9	17
	Bg2	8½–15			3	2	1.5		5.5	4.6	0.8	0.2		0.1	2.7	37
	Cg	15–30			<1	<1	0.1		5.3	4.6	0.1	0.1		0.1	0.8	38
		30+			<1	<1	0.1		6.7	6.5	2.8			0.1	0.8	Sat.
La 109 (p. 46)	A	0–6			7	5	3.4		6.2	5.4	4.8	0.1	0.1	0.1	5.4	95
	Bg	6–9			5	5	3.3		6.2	5.5	5.5	0.1	0.1	0.2	5.1	Sat.
	Cg	9–14			3	2	1.8		6.1	5.3	1.4	0.1		0.1	2.7	56
		14–17					94.1		5.6	4.8						
Hesketh Complex																
La 125 (p. 65)	Ag	0–14			52	46	12.0	4	7.7	7.7						
	B/Cg	14–21			66	18	4.1	8.2	8.3	7.9						
	Cg	21–42			53	17	4.4	6.8	8.4	7.9						
La 107 (p. 65)	A	0–12			54	20	5.7	7.4	7.9	7.4						
	B/C	12–19			40	7	2.0	9.3	8.4	7.7						
	Cg1	19–26			3	2	0.2	7.5	8.5	7.7						
	Cg2	26+			36	6	2.8	8.0	8.3	7.6						
La 111 (p. 66)	Ap	0–9		43	32	17	7.1	3.2	7.6	7.2						
	B/Cg	9–15			23	1	0.5	6.9	8.3	7.7						
	Cg1	15–25			28	2	1.3	8.3	8.4	7.8						
	Cg2	25–33			46	22	4.7	8.0	7.9	7.7						
		33–60					65.4		4.6	4.5						
		60+	7	6	69	24	8.3		5.8	5.7						

TABLE 13 (continued)

Profile No.	Horizon	Depth in.	Sand 200 μ-2 mm.	Sand 50 μ-200 μ	Silt 2 μ-50 μ	Clay <2 μ	Loss on Ignition	CaCO₃, %	pH H₂O 1:2.5	pH CaCl₂ M/100	Ca	Mg	K	Na	Cation Exchange Capacity m.e./100 gm.	Percentage Base-saturation
Lea Series																
La 121 (p. 53)	Ag	0–8	11	24	35	28	18·0		5·4	4·8	13·1	0·9	0·3	0·2	30·3	48
	Ebg	8–21			31	15	2·5	0·2	6·9	6·2	3·7	0·6		0·1	5·4	81
	Cg	21+			28	33	3·0	0·6	7·4	6·7						
Newport Series																
La 122 (p. 34)	A	0–9	12	42	28	16	12·7		6·2	5·7	15·4	0·7	0·1	0·1	18·1	91
	B	9–15	14	44	24	6	7·6		5·2	4·4	4·0	0·3	0·1	0·1	12·1	36
	C	15+			21	6	1·3		5·5	4·5	0·9	0·1		0·1	2·2	50
Oaklands Series																
SD 52/1465 (p. 56)	Ag	0–11			36	42	20·6		5·7	5·2	9·3	1·2	0·2	0·2	14·3	77
	Btg or Bg	11–16			33	46	4·7		5·9	5·3	18·8	6·7	0·2	0·2	26·5	98
	Cgca	16–36			34	47	6·6	4·3	7·8	7·2						
Rufford Series																
La 104 (p. 37)	Ap(g)	0–9			14	13	4·1		6·3	5·6	5·6	0·3	0·1	0·1	7·2	83
	Bg	9–13			8	5	1·4		6·0	5·3	1·8	0·3	0·1	0·1	2·8	75
	Bg/Cg	13–17			28	33	4·5		6·4	5·9	7·7	1·5		0·2	11·7	72
	Cg	17+			32	34	4·0	0·2	7·1	6·6						
Salop Series																
La 131 (p. 55)	A(g)	0–6	10	23	38	26	7·8		5·9	5·1	8·9	0·5	0·1	0·2	14·2	68
	Ag or Ebg	6–13			38	25	5·2		6·1	5·2	7·4	0·9	0·1	0·2	11·4	75
	Btg	13–21			28	49	5·5		6·3	5·7	7·7	2·8	0·1	0·1	14·2	76
	C(g)	21–42			29	42	4·4	1·6	8·0	7·3						
	C(g)ca	42+			37	34	4·0	9·9	8·6	8·0						

TABLE 13 (continued)

Profile No.	Horizon	Depth in.	Sand 200μ–2 mm	Sand 50μ–200μ	Silt 2μ–50μ	Clay <2μ	Loss on Ignition	CaCO₃ %	pH H₂O 1:2.5	pH CaCl₂ M/100	Ca	Mg	K	Na	Cation Exchange Capacity m.e./100 gm.	Percentage Base-saturation
Salwick Series																
La 100 (p. 51)	Ap	0–5	35	26	22	14	6.8		5.4	4.6	4.3	0.2	0.2	0.1	11.3	42
	A	5–10			27	19	5.5		5.8	5.1	5.0	0.2	0.1	0.1	11.2	48
	Eb(g)	10–15			24	16	3.0		5.5	4.6	3.7	0.3	0.1	0.1	7.3	56
	Bt(g)	15–18			26	28	3.9		5.7	5.0	4.9	0.5	0.1	0.1	9.0	61
	Bt/C(g)	18–28			46	32	3.6		6.1	5.6	6.7	1.3	0.1	0.1	11.0	75
Sollom Complex																
La 88 (p. 39)	Ap	0–8	55	31	8	4	17.7		4.9	4.2	9.1		0.1	0.2	27.5	36
	Ea	8–14			1	<1	0.8		5.2	4.5	0.5				1.1	45
	Bfe	14–24			1	<1	0.7		5.3	4.7	0.4				0.8	64
	B/Cg	24–33	78	22	<1	<1	0.5		5.7	5.1	0.5				0.8	60
La 114 (p. 40)	Ap	0–8			13	12	11.0		5.8	5.2	7.2	0.3		0.1	11.7	63
	Ea1	8–13			6	10	3.2		5.7	4.9	3.5	0.3		0.1	9.0	43
	Ea2	13–18			2	5	2.1		5.9	5.1	3.0	0.2	0.1	0.1	5.1	63
	B/Cg	18–20			25	30	4.3		6.0	5.2	6.7	1.0	0.1	0.2	12.5	63
	C(g)1	20–25			28	43	5.1		5.8	5.1	6.6	1.9	0.1	0.2	13.0	67
	C(g)2	25 +			26	42	4.5		5.8	5.1	4.3	3.8			12.4	68
La 112 (p. 40)		0–7			16	5	12.7		5.5	4.8	4.0	0.1	0.1	0.1	15.2	28
		7–15			14	9	12.4		4.8	4.2	1.6	0.1		0.1	16.7	11
		15–18					60.3		4.4	3.7						
		18–29							4.4	3.9	0.1				0.9	22
		29–40			1	4	0.4		4.0	3.7	0.2				0.8	38
		40 +			1	1	1.3		2.9	2.7	0.2	0.2		0.1	12.6	4

CHAPTER VIII

Agriculture and Horticulture

Climatic conditions are generally favourable to the production of crops but several distinct systems of agriculture have arisen because of very different kinds of soils present, some of which permit the production of highly remunerative crops. An average rainfall of between 30 and 35 in. per annum is sufficient for the production of many crops and droughts are rare. Being a west coastal region, winters are relatively mild and are followed by seasons in which moderate falls of rain are frequent so that, drainage and soil permitting, conditions for growth are good. The district is relatively early and is particularly suited to vegetables and potatoes. The winds, however, often blow strongly from the southwest distorting the shapes of trees and shrubs on the exposed plain. The wind, blowing over the sea, is salt-laden but any effect it may have on crops has not been determined, although farmers consider the salt it carries may be beneficial to sugar beet. That such winds may contribute salt to the land is suggested by the amount of chloride (calculated as salt) found in the leaf litter from the coniferous plantations adjacent to the coast (p. 45).

Small and medium-sized farms are common but large holdings are few. Most farms are rented and much of the land is in the hands of owners of large estates such as Scarisbrick, Croxteth and Church Commissioners Estates. There is a tendency to amalgamate holdings on these estates and the acreage of individual farm units is likely to become larger than the present average size.

The Ribble estuary conveniently divides the district surveyed into two for discussion of the agricultural pattern.

Agriculture of South Fylde

The main enterprises can be grouped under the general heading of dairy-with-arable and contrasts with the mainly arable region south of the Ribble. The predominant soils in the South Fylde of agricultural value are derived from either boulder clay, Downholland Silt or peat. Generally speaking, farms on these soils have one acre in ten growing cereals, the remaining nine being under grass much of which has never been ploughed. The imperfectly and poorly drained soils of the Salwick and Clifton series on the medium-textured boulder clay are periodically reseeded and the crop is invariably mown for hay or silage. The stocking rate is traditionally very high and many farms carry a dairy cow, or the equivalent in young stock, beef or sheep, on less than $1\frac{1}{2}$ acres.

Hay is the most widely used form of winter fodder produced but the acreage of kale sown broadcast for the dairy herd is increasing. The difficulty of obtaining labour has necessitated the construction of farm buildings planned to minimize labour requirements, for example permitting the self-feeding of silage, and it has also encouraged the adoption of more economic systems of conservation and feeding.

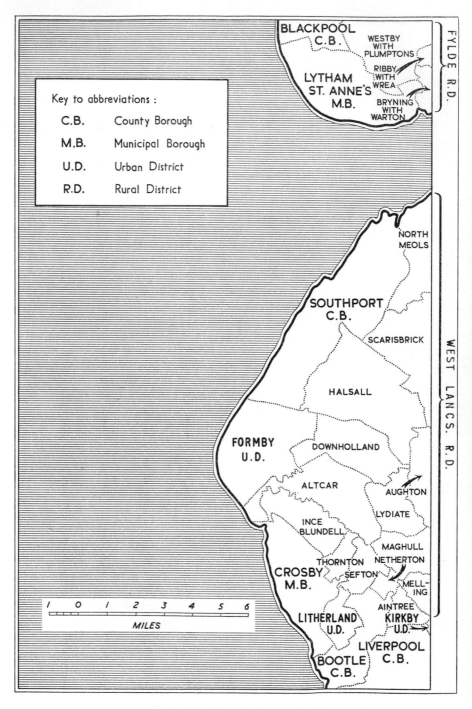

Fig. 8. Administrative Boundaries.

Cropping on Lytham, Peel and Ballam Mosses, where the soils vary from the deep peats of the Altcar complex to the peaty silt loams of the Downholland complex, follows a system of approximately four years grass followed by three cereal crops and one potato crop. Yields of cereals in excess of 2 tons per acre are obtainable under good management. The dairy-with-arable farms are mostly owner-occupied and, by standards pertinent to the Fylde, are large with acreages normally in excess of 150 acres. Approximately 40 per cent. of land of the average farm is on mossland, the remainder being on mineral soil, so that the arable enterprises on the mossland are normally supplementary to dairying and sheep farming. Farms on the edge of the mosslands where the very poorly drained Lea and Oaklands series occur have a higher proportion of cereals in the rotation. Past overcropping with cereals has resulted in widespread infestation with couch-grass (*Agropyron repens*) but chemical methods of control have now lessened this problem.

The blown sand along the coast, giving rise to the Dune Sand complex and Formby series is of little agricultural use and, where not of amenity value, is rapidly being used for urban development. The sea-washed marshes and the marshes behind the sea-walls with soils of the Hesketh complex are used mainly for sheep and cattle grazing. Tile drainage is ineffective because the high silt content of the soil causes rapid silting up and open ditches, which require regular upkeep, are necessary. Around Great Marton horticulture is an important industry and the district maintains an intensive horticultural production with a flourishing glasshouse industry (p. 100).

Agriculture south of the Ribble

This area is moderately undulating with small outcrops of till and sandstone, which, however, have little influence on the farming pattern, and arable crops predominate with emphasis on the production of potatoes, cereals, sugar beet and vegetables grown on a variety of soils which respond well to intensive cropping. Livestock is a very secondary enterprise and many farms carry none at all.

The soils of the Sollom, Rufford and Astley Hall series are easily worked and capable of giving high returns from the intensive cultivation of arable crops, all of which grow excellently and, indeed, under good management two crops can be taken during the year. The soils are inherently of low fertility but respond strongly to sound husbandry, generous liming and fertilizing. The coarse-textured soil overlying the boulder clay is permeable and open drainage ditches are rarely seen but tile drainage schemes are widespread. Such is the value of the land that hedges are infrequent and many fields are cultivated to the very edge of the road.

The mossland is bleak, thinly populated and, except for game cover, is largely devoid of hedges and trees. The soils of the Altcar and Turbary Moor complexes are almost completely under arable, producing excellent yields of corn, potatoes, sugar beet and vegetables (*Plate IVa*). The full potential of the mosses can only be realized by sound drainage systems and adequate liming and fertilizing of the peat. Drainage is the key to farming and the extensive flooding in the 1950s was directly due to the gradual deterioration of the gravity system of drainage with outfalls to the sea; similar disastrous floods occurred in Martin Mere to the east. As a result, the Crossens Drainage Scheme, covering 36,000 acres, was approved and is now operational, the water being pumped into the sea at

Crossens, north of Southport (Prus-Chacinski and Harris, 1963). The river Alt system, however, is still a gravity system with outfall gates at Hightown, but has not provided a permanent solution to the drainage of the farmland and, before long, the question of installing pumps will have to be considered.

Large areas of the Hesketh complex on the alluvium in the Ribble estuary have been reclaimed by the construction of embankments and excellent land of high cropping potential has resulted. The production of cash crops is of prime importance and, furthermore, the grassland carrying mainly cattle and a few sheep is probably the most highly stocked area in the surveyed district south of the Ribble. The area of the Downholland and Altcar complexes on the alluvium around Altcar is similarly devoted to the production of cash crops.

The blown sand adjoining the coast is inherently of very low fertility and much of it is used for recreation purposes. It is thus in direct contrast to the intensively cropped Sollom, Rufford and Astley Hall soils associated with the Shirdley Hill Sand, and with the mossland and alluvial soils. Much of the Formby series is poor "heathy" permanent grassland, although ley grass, dairy herds and some cash crops indicate possible lines of utilization and the potential productivity of this flat expanse of relatively infertile sand bordering the mossland.

The principal crops grown in the surveyed district south of the Ribble are potatoes, cereals, vegetables, sugar beet and short-term leys for hay. More than half the cereal acreage is harvested by the combine harvester and the numerous grain drying and storage plants indicate the high level of investment in cereal growing. Continued increases in yields are a direct result of the introduction of new varieties and more generous manurial treatment. The decline in the popularity of oats is striking and is a result of competition from spring barley which is now more freely used in feeding stock, is more easily grown and gives higher yields. Barley yields of up to 2 tons per acre are common with an average yield of approximately $1\frac{1}{4}$ tons per acre while oats yield 27 cwt per acre on the average. The yields from oats were low and failures were common because of serious attacks of cereal-root eelworm. Lodging, especially in oats, makes harvesting a difficulty in growing cereals in south-west Lancashire particularly on the sandy soils of the Sollom and Rufford series and on the mosses, but it can be overcome by the use of varieties with stronger straw. By decreasing the acidity so that the pH values of the soils of the mosslands are between 5·5 and 6·0, barley and wheat can be grown where formerly only crops of oats and rye could be taken; little rye is now grown. Although barley lodges badly, even in that condition it is easily picked up by the combine harvester.

Wheat is an important crop and the acreage remains steady. Winter wheat is favoured, though more spring wheat is grown on the mosslands to avoid the losses due to frost lifting the soil. Yields of wheat up to $2\frac{1}{2}$ tons per acre are common with an average of between $1\frac{1}{2}$ and 2 tons for winter wheats and between $1\frac{1}{2}$ and $1\frac{3}{4}$ tons per acre for spring wheats.

The south-west Lancashire farmer is a skilful potato grower and his knowledge has been accumulated over a very long period for, in this country, the potato was first grown commercially in Lancashire and has been a farm crop since the beginning of the 19th century. Although it still is the leading crop, it has declined considerably in popularity because of the widespread occurrence of potato-root eelworm (*Heterodera rostochicensis*), particularly on the Sollom, Rufford and Astley Hall series. The infestation was a direct result of over-cropping and the pest is particularly difficult to eradicate. In an area where the crop was vital, the serious effects on the farming economy were lessened by the profits from a range of other crops and, in more recent years, by the local demand for peas by the canning industry established in Liverpool. In the early part of the century, wart disease was rife and ruined many crops of potatoes. An official Potato Testing Station was established near Ormskirk where (until the ravages of potato-root eelworm caused its abandonment) all new varieties were tested for susceptibility to the disease. The disease is now uncommon because the use of non-immune varieties on scheduled land is prohibited and the farmer recognizes the futility of growing susceptible varieties.

Potato blight (*Phytothera infestans*) is not a serious disease in the district, and a decade ago it did not appear until the end of the growing season so that burning-off the haulm was sufficient control. Recently, however, it has appeared earlier in the growing season and spraying to control it has become necessary. A small proportion of the potato acreage is planted with early and second early varieties but the larger part is in maincrop production. The early crop is planted chiefly on the Sollom soils around Halsall and Scarisbrick and although it is not a particularly early area, the first crops can sometimes be lifted by mid-June to be followed by the bulk of the crop at the end of the month. Formerly Ulster Chieftain was the popular variety because its short haulm allowed cabbages or savoys to be interplanted but, as this necessitated a great deal of hand labour, its popularity declined rapidly. The most extensively grown variety at present is Ulster Prince, although Arran Pilot is commonly found.

There is no dominant second early variety. Craig's Royal is widely planted but is not completely satisfactory and the maincrop varieties Majestic and Dr. McIntosh are frequently lifted "greentop" as second earlies. The so-called "earlies" of the mossland (Craig's Royal and Home Guard) reach the market at the same time as these second earlies. Majestic is the principal maincrop variety and yields about 13 tons per acre. Dr. McIntosh, giving about the same average yield, is increasing in popularity and King Edward VII and Redskin are commonly grown on the mossland. Unfortunately, King Edward VII is not immune to wart disease and as it yields only 9–10 tons per acre it is unsuitable for large-scale planting. A practice peculiar to south-west Lancashire is the "cutting" of seed—a practice which considerably reduces the amount of seed required. It is, however, declining because it has been found that unless seed is exceptionally dear, the cost of cutting is greater than the value of the seed saved.

Increased mechanization has resulted in more rapid planting and harvesting but the need for further saving of labour to reduce costs is apparent. Both pallet handling and indoor storage save labour and, to some extent, reduce damage to the tubers—a matter of increasing importance as the pre-packed trade develops.

The time of lifting the early crop is determined by the price obtainable and accordingly it may or may not be economic to lift when the yield is only 2 tons per acre. As the season advances yields of up to 5 or 6 tons per acre are common.

One-year leys, largely of Italian ryegrass, are grown for hay, much of which is sold in east Lancashire, Cheshire and the west Midlands. Second crops, taken when the weather permits, yield up to 3 tons per acre of moderately good hay. On some farms three-year leys have been introduced to be cut for hay in the first year and to be subsequently used for grazing by both beef and dairy cattle before the land is returned to arable cropping. By this means the rotation is lengthened in order to reduce the effects of potato-root eelworm and to maintain the organic-matter content and structure of the soil. Root crops are not extensively grown for fodder although a few acres of kale are to be found on the few farms with dairy interests.

In general, crop production is based on sound cultivations and generous manuring but it sometimes suffers from opportunism which may lead the farmer to ignore the sound tenets of good husbandry and often the more profitable crops are grown too frequently. The sandy soils of the Sollom complex and others associated with Shirdley Hill Sand and the organic soils of the Altcar and Turbary Moor complexes of the mossland lend themselves to such exploitation. The potato-root eelworm infestation, for example, followed excessive potato cropping and necessitated an adjustment of the farming system and a drastic reduction of the acreage of this important and valuable crop.

The countryside presents a picture of good husbandry, thorough cultivations and clean crops. The use of herbicides to control weeds has extended rapidly, with a considerable saving in labour costs. Farming on the mosses in particular has benefited from their use for these soils are readily infested with annual weeds, the commonest being redshank (*Polygonum persicaria*). Weed control also enables a much wider variety of crops to be grown, including root crops such as carrots, red beet, sugar beet and peas—all of which were liable to be smothered in their early stages of growth by the fierce growth of weeds.

The use of farmyard manure on arable land has steadily declined because of the gradual disappearance of the horses and cows formerly kept in the numerous city dairies in Liverpool. Very large quantities of farmyard manure were brought from Liverpool and some still is, but many farmers use none at all. Generous applications of artificial fertilizers are commonly given, and no decrease is yet apparent in the high level of production. Compound fertilizers are normally used with nitrogenous top dressings for green crops and cereals. Fertilizers high in potassium are also used, particularly on the soils of the Sollom complex where the natural supply of potash is low and where potash-sensitive crops such as potatoes, peas and brassicas are to be grown. As a result of former generous manuring, the phosphate status is generally satisfactory, having been increased from a naturally low degree, particularly on the organic soils of the mossland. There is now a tendency to reduce applications and to use compound fertilizers that have a lower content of phosphate. Dressings of from 10 to 14 cwt per acre of compound fertilizer are used for potatoes, sugar beet and some of the vegetable crops. Cereals may receive either 3 cwt per acre of compound fertilizer in the seed bed or 4 cwt per acre of a nitrogenous top dressing according to the stage in the rotation at which it is applied. Winter wheat responds well to the spring application of nitrogenous top dressings.

The lime status of the soils varies considerably but liming is widely practiced on the mossland and the coarse-textured, humose Sollom soils. It is on these soils, however, that over-liming has occurred, resulting in the appearance of symptoms in plants of deficiencies of trace elements, of which manganese, boron and magnesium are the most frequently observed. Manganese deficiency is overcome by spraying the growing crop with manganese sulphate and this is becoming a routine procedure with spring cereals.

The use of marl or calcareous clay to ameliorate the condition of the soil was widespread in Lancashire long before the development of the lime and artificial fertilizer industries. Marling was a common practice on the fine-textured soils that were acid as well as on the sandy soils which were subject to blowing. On both it was used as a source of lime and nutrients and on the sandy soils it helped to reduce erosion by wind.

John Holt (1795) states that "Marle is the great article of fertilization, and the foundation of the improvements in the agriculture of this country; and this earth, or fossil, is fortunately wanting in but few places."

The extensive deposits of boulder clay throughout the Fylde and the south-west Lancashire plain provided the source of the marl and the numerous abandoned pits testify to the importance of marling in the agricultural history of these areas. There are few fields in these areas of the Fylde that are without a marl pit. However, a large number were dug from which no marl was extracted because of the presence of springs, sandy horizons, or pockets of stones and boulders. The marl was not transported far and was often spread over the field containing the pit from which it was dug.

Decalcification of the surface horizons of the boulder clay and the subsequent accumulation of calcium carbonate in the upper parts of the C horizon gave rise to a calcareous clay at no great depth which was easily dug out and spread on the surface at varying rates to correct a tendency to acidity and to improve aggregation of the surface soil.

Holt describes the process of marling and comments on the cost, methods and time of application. "The summer is the best season for laying marle upon the land sometimes immediately after a crop of hay has been taken. Its effects upon the grass are soon visible, from the rich verdure which it produces. Long experience has sufficiently proved the propriety of the general practice of the county; which is, to lay the marle upon grasslands, the older the better; the sward and grass united causes a fermentation and putrefaction which seems necessary to produce the proper effect."

"The quantity laid on is from two to three or three and a half cubic roods of 64 yards to every statue acre; the expense of which is according to the distance carried if in the same field or within the distance of sixty rods on the average at about eight pounds per acre. It is reckoned a much better practice to have the marling repeated with a gentle covering than a strong thick coat of marle which is intended to last a number of years. If these dressings of marle were repeated more frequently (and no husbandry has been found to pay better) the lands in Lancashire in general would be found much more productive".

"The marle should partake both of the one summer's sun and one winter's frosts at least. After being exposed to the effects of the weather in large lumps it begins to fall or melt; the particles appear unctuous and soapy and the quality of the substance seems quite changed from its original state. Then in the ensuing spring, it should be divided (the parts now separate with ease), and equally distributed upon every part of the surface, that is, with facility, effected by harrows, etc. after which it is usually ploughed under; but, if permitted to remain a year or two longer, the lands would be more improved in the issue, by the length of time given previous to the marle being ploughed in. But the marle does not produce its full effects upon the soil, till intermixed and incorporated by a repetition of ploughings, and an intermixture of dung, or other manure, for marle is not effectual without such addition."

As well as being used on the finer-textured soils marl was also spread on sandier soils of the Sollom complex and on the peat land to reduce both acidity and wind erosion. Evidence of the practice is to be found in the widespread occurrence of loamy surface horizons with numerous pebbles and cobbles. On these soils the base status is substantially increased, the acidity is lowered and the increase in the clay content of the surface soil tends to reduce dessication and wind blowing.

Cattle farming is of little importance although there is some dairying around Southport, but the interest in beef production is growing, particularly where the three-year ley is part of the rotation. The numbers of sheep kept on farms are small but hill sheep are wintered on those farms adjoining the salt marshes. Some farmers specialize in the large-scale breeding and fattening of pigs and a few pigs are kept on most farms. Poultry farming is widespread although free range poultry are infrequently found and most of the birds are kept in batteries or on deep litter. Laying flocks are dominant and the production of broilers is less common; a number of specialist poultry-keepers produce breeding stock and eggs for hatching.

Skilled and permanent labour is scarce but casual labour is fairly freely available from the industrial regions. Industry, however, competes directly with farming in the labour market and the labour required on farms is being reduced by increased mechanization and the use of labour-saving devices. There is, however, a tendency to buy expensive machinery which is in use only for very short periods and although co-operation would, in theory, be beneficial it is not generally favoured.

South-west Lancashire is favoured by the proximity of a very large consumer market able to absorb most of the local products. The advantages of a large local demand for produce are, however, partially offset by the problems of urban expansion and the need for more building land, which is particularly great to the north of Liverpool. Associated with this extension of towns into the countryside is the very serious problem of trespass with the inevitable damage to both crops and animals that results.

The Horticultural Industry

Before the 1914–18 war the acreage of glass was very small but from the early 1920s onwards, it increased rapidly. The industry is concentrated at Marton Moss, Blackpool, and between the Ribble estuary and Southport where the atmospheric pollution is low, the intensity of light is high and the predominant soils of the Downholland and Altcar complexes and of the Lea and Oaklands series have humose or peaty surface horizons. The acreage of glass per holding varies from a few square feet to several acres, though the average is probably about ¼ acre; the holding may have an additional ¼ acre of land not under glass. Winter lettuce, tomatoes and chrysanthemums are the principal crops grown in the annual rotation.

Sowing for the autumn crop of lettuce starts at the end of August and the crop is ready for market in late October and early November, somewhat later sowings being made for the Christmas market. For the spring crop the soil is sterilized and flooded, and farmyard manure, lime and fertilizers are applied, the seed is then sown from October onwards to ensure a continuous supply in the early months of the year. Watering methods vary considerably depending on the soil characters and required time of harvest and, when the soil is humose and moist, overhead damping is all that is required in sunny weather. The fungus diseases Mildew, *Botrytis*, and attacks by symphilids cause heavy losses at times and marginal scorch or "tip-burn" can be troublesome and difficult to control.

The earliest crop of tomatoes is grown with the aid of mercury-vapour lighting in the propagating houses, the seeds being sown during November and December so that picking starts about mid-April. For most growers, however, the season is shorter as the crop follows the clearance of the spring lettuce. One of the main problems under such intensive use is the control of disease and some form of sterilization is necessary. Houses not already sterilized for the previous crop are steamed or chemically treated, carbon bisulphide being favoured by many growers. Potato-root eelworm and other root diseases are difficult to control in soils with a high water-table that cannot be dried out sufficiently for effective sterilization. Steaming is not always favoured on peat as tomatoes tend to grow rank after such treatment while chemical sterilization, unless carefully carried out, gives indifferent results. Tomato Mosaic can cause heavy losses and Leaf Mould and *Botrytis* are at times very prevalent.

Chrysanthemums frequently follow the tomato crop in the glasshouse rotation, the plants being grown in well-sheltered sites during the summer months and brought into the glasshouses in September in order that they may flower in December. Recently many growers have successfully used the technique of striking cuttings late and direct planting.

Many growers, particularly around Blackpool, inter-plant the lettuce crop in January with sweet peas. The system is liable to cause some reduction of the following tomato crop, for if prices are satisfactory the sweet peas may remain until early June.

A few specialist mushroom growers operate in this area; the crop is grown on several nurseries in addition to the crops already mentioned, and also on a few farms.

Many glasshouse holdings have additional land not under glass on which early lettuce, cauliflowers and chrysanthemums are grown in sheltered plots sometimes no larger than ¼ acre, and a wide range of salad and vegetable crops is also grown extensively on market gardens and farms.

On the peaty soils around Banks, especially on the smaller holdings, early lettuce and cauliflowers are extensively grown, together with main crop celery and beetroot. On this moisture-retentive soil, good drainage is necessary and, because over-liming causes manganese deficiency, particularly in red beetroot, cauliflower and lettuce, the soil is maintained at a slightly acid reaction with the pH value kept at about 5·9.

Celery is often grown between the rows of lettuce and when the lettuce crop has been taken the soil around the celery can be drawn up into ridges. Self-blanching celery is only grown on a small scale with the use of overhead irrigation.

Lettuce is also extensively grown as an outdoor crop on both peaty and mineral soils. The fields for lettuce around Banks are planted as early as March and cutting continues, from early May throughout the summer months. *Botrytis* sometimes causes heavy losses and, later in the season, aphids on leaves and roots are a problem.

Although spinach is extensively grown elsewhere in the county, only a small acreage, grown on contract for canning and quick freezing, is devoted to it in the surveyed district. Canning and freezing firms exert considerable influence in the district and peas and beans are widely grown for them. Pea vining today is mechanized; the whole plants are mechanically harvested and transported to local factory-owned viners where the peas are shelled for transport to the factory.

The carrot acreage has increased considerably during recent years, particularly on peat soils, and red beetroot is another widely grown crop; many growers meeting the demand for cooked beetroot by boiling and peeling it on their holdings. Brussels sprouts, cabbages and cauliflowers are extensively grown, particularly on farms in rotation with farm crops, but on smaller holdings preference is given to cauliflower plants, raised in glasshouses, to mature in late May and June.

Asparagus is a crop grown around Formby by specialists where sites are levelled in the dunes and one-year old crowns are planted with cut marram grass pushed in vertically between each row to provide shelter and protection from blowing sand. Most growers apply farmyard manure but very little artificial fertilizer is used and weeds are controlled by herbicides.

The general trends in horticulture are associated with the increasing demand for canned and frozen vegetables which has resulted in a steady increase in the acreage of crops grown on contract for these trades and the adaptation of cropping techniques to suit the changing times.

Land Use and Farming Practices on Mossland

The unfavourable conditions for habitation and cultivation ensured that the mossland remained in its natural state for a longer time than adjacent land and little of the history of settlement can be gleaned from early writings or maps; most authors commented only on the more extreme physical conditions and 17th and 18th century maps are of too small a scale to give reliable details of land use.

Although the land reclaimed in connection with the former Martin Mere is probably the most extensive area, other schemes, notably improvements to the river Alt carried out after 1789, enabled land farther south to be reclaimed; the Alt works included artificial channels in the parishes of Altcar and Halsall as well as changes in the main course of the river. Some documents refer to the existence of minor meres and pools, namely Gettern, Rainbage and Hainshoot Meres and Black and White Otter Pools. Little is known of drainage operations on these waters which at the beginning of the 19th century had a collective area of only about 100 acres. As well as improving major natural water courses and introducing artificial drainage schemes, problems of field drainage and building construction had to be overcome before mossland could be effectively occupied and farmed. The earliest settlements and communications were located near the eastern margin and it is evident that at first mossland was farmed in conjunction with farmsteads sited on the mineral soils. Reference to the few and incomplete 18th century estate maps suggests that by about 1770 occupation had spread across the more easily accessible parts, particularly near Scarisbrick, Altcar, Churchtown and Halsall. Not until the Ordnance Survey maps of 1845, however, was there a reliable guide to the extent of cultivation and the location of buildings. These maps show that the greatest extent (about 700 acres) of uncultivated mossland at that time was west of Tarleton though there were several smaller mosses near Altcar. Fields over much of the area were smaller than now and were separated by ditches. Several writers of the mid-19th century describe methods of reclamation and cultivation which included the removal of some 4–5 ft. of turf to reach the lower and more "productive" layers; the cut peat was used for fuel. It was common practice to cut and pare the upper layers of peat after a series of open drains had been dug and in some instances sod or wooden drains were installed. After the cut layers had been burned and the land ploughed two or three successive crops of oats would be taken, and finally the land would be marled before being cropped with wheat, potatoes and oats.

Several factors undoubtedly led to increasing use being made of mossland. For example, the rapid growth of Liverpool and other urban centres during the 19th century stimulated a demand for arable crops; at that time, also, great use was made of the Leeds–Liverpool Canal as a means of transporting crops to the towns as well as waste from the towns to the mosses. Night soil was used as a top dressing and waste material was used to make new and essential roads across the mosses being developed for agriculture. Beesley, writing in 1849, considers that after 1835 agriculture revived in Lancashire and "some degree of the commercial spirit began to animate the stagnating genius of agricultural society".

Districts east and north of Southport were not much influenced until after the opening of the railway to Liverpool in 1850 and five years later to Manchester. The town then expanded greatly and there was no doubt some extention of farming inland and to the east of Southport. Nonetheless the area between Banks and Tarleton remained relatively undeveloped until a much later date and although the last to be reclaimed it is now utilized for intensive market gardening.

Land-use patterns on the mossland, therefore, reflect the difficulties in reclaiming a naturally unfavourable environment. Problems in reclaiming and farming mossland are not only related to drainage but include the creation and maintenance of access roads and the provision of adequate buildings. Peat is an unsatisfactory material on which to build, and numerous tilted, foundering and even derelict farm buildings are to be found; to some extent the problem can be overcome by building on stilts, piles or rafts but such methods add to the expense of construction and elaborate farmsteads are lacking. From another point of view the instability can be regarded as an asset in that mossland is unlikely to attract urban development and its agricultural use is practically assured for a long time.

The rotation of crops on most mossland farms is normally of three courses, and consists of potatoes, followed by cereals, and then seeds from which one or sometimes two cuts of hay are obtained. Occasionally the grass is left down for two consecutive years and often two consecutive crops of cereals are taken. On many farms brassicas, sugar beet and carrots have been introduced into the rotation, often in place of potatoes. In a few instances stock for fattening or dairy cows are kept. The numbers of grazing stock, however, are limited on farms where intensive arable farming is practised and the stock-carrying capacity is affected by the difficulty of maintaining a good sward.

The inclusion of a one or two-year ley in the rotation is considered of great importance in the farming pattern, for the grass and clover roots help to maintain the open, crumb structure of the soil. The structure tends to disappear in a system of continuous arable cropping, and the soil, becoming light and powdery, blows away in dry windy weather. During wet periods, however, the aggregates break down and run together to form a relatively impervious surface layer thus providing an added problem of drainage.

In the past considerable quantities of stable manure were obtainable from Liverpool but this source of organic matter is lost and, furthermore, as only limited numbers of stock are kept on the average moss farm, little farmyard manure is available for use today.

The potato crop receives 8 to 12 cwt of a complete fertilizer depending on the previous crop, whether grass or cereal, the heavier dressing being used in the latter instance. The acreage of winter wheat following potatoes is gradually increasing due to improved drainage of the mossland, and the introduction of stronger-strawed varieties and this crop generally receives a top dressing in the spring of up to 4 cwt per acre of a nitrogenous fertilizer. Similarly 2 to 3 cwt per acre of a nitrogenous fertilizer is used on spring wheat and on barley after potatoes. However, if these are second straw crops then a complete fertilizer is given at the rate of 3 to 4 cwt per acre. The acreage of oats, once the main cereal on mossland, is now rapidly declining and is being replaced by the more profitable barley crop.

The normal treatment for the seeds hay is to apply 3 cwt per acre of a compound fertilizer in spring, sometimes with a further application of 2 cwt per acre of a nitrogenous fertilizer after cutting if the aftermath is to be grazed or a second cut taken.

High acidity is one of the chief problems associated with mossland soils and, although heavy dressings of lime have been given in the past, most of the soils covered by this survey are noticeably acid; this fact has no doubt contributed to the use of the land for oats and potatoes in the past, both being comparatively tolerant of acid soil conditions. With the introduction of barley and brassicas, which demand more alkaline conditions, it has become necessary for heavier and more frequent applications of lime to be given.

Theoretically, lime requirements of 10 to 15 tons per acre are common but peat soils crop well at pH values lower than those of mineral soils. The acidity can be partly corrected by giving two applications each of about 5 tons per acre, one being ploughed in and the other applied to the surface after ploughing. After these initial treatments, a dressing of 3 to 4 tons per acre of ground limestone is generally necessary every fourth year to maintain the reaction at a satisfactory level.

A serious problem of mossland is that of weed infestation, the main weeds being redshank, corn spurrey (*Spergula arvensis*), sorrel, knot grass (*Polygonum aviculare*), groundsel (*Senecio vulgaris*), hemp-nettle (*Galeopsia* spp.) and chickweed (*Stellaria media*).

By far the most serious of these are redshank and, to a lesser degree, hemp-nettle and chickweed which find an ideal habitat on mossland. Unless they are controlled by spraying or frequent inter-row cultivation weeds rapidly gain the upper hand. Sprays are available for controlling weeds but there is no doubt that the best method is good cultivation, which is only possible on well drained land.

The frequency with which potatoes occur in the rotation, coupled with the increase in acreage of the crop during the war years, led to the spread of potato-root eelworm. Potatoes grown on mossland appear to be able to withstand far greater numbers of eelworm than those grown on mineral soils. This has tended to aggravate the problem because by the time yields are seriously affected, the eelworm population has increased to such an extent that a rest of ten years or more from this crop becomes necessary.

The problem has given rise to the need for alternative crops in order to limit the appearance of potatoes in rotations. Brassicas (cabbage, cauliflower, sprouts, etc.) are the most popular alternatives. All grow well on peat soils provided the land has been under cultivation for a number of years. The crop next in popularity is carrots, which are often grown on contract for the pre-packing trade. Sugar beet is a crop recently introduced into the district and yields well on the deeper organic soils and the growing both of this crop and carrots on this kind of land has been greatly facilitated by the introduction of pre-emergence weed killers.

References

AVERY, B. W. (1956). A classification of British soils. *Trans. 6th int. Congr. Soil Sci.* E, 279–85.

BAXENDELL, J. (1935). *Annual Report of the Fernley Observatory.* Southport.

BEESLEY, G. (1849). *Report on the state of Agriculture in Lancashire.* Preston.

BLOOMFIELD, C. (1951). Experiments on the mechanism of gley formation. *J. Soil Sci.* 2, 196–221.

BOUYOUCOS, G. J. (1951). A recalibration of the Bouyoucos hydrometer method for the mechanical analysis of soils. *Agron. J.* 43, 434–8.

BOWDEN, K. F. (1953). Physical oceanography of the Irish Sea. In: *Merseyside, a scientific study.* British Association for the Advancement of Science.

BRAUN-BLANQUET, J. (1932). *Plant sociology.* McGraw-Hill, New York.

CROMPTON, E. (1966). *The soils of the Preston district of Lancashire.* Mem. Soil Surv. Gt Br.

CROMPTON, E. and OSMOND, D. A. (1954). *The soils of the Wem district of Shropshire.* Mem. Soil Surv. Gt Br.

DE RANCE, C. E. (1870). *Geology of the country between Liverpool and Southport.* Mem. geol. Surv. U.K.

DE RANCE, C. E. (1883). Notes on the Post-glacial geology of the country around Southport. *Nature, Lond.* 28, 490–1.

DUCHAUFOUR, PH. (1960). *Précis de Pédologie.* Masson, Paris.

GRESSWELL, R. K. (1953). *Sandy shores in South Lancashire.* Liverpool U.P.

GRESSWELL, R. K. (1958). The post-glacial raised beach in Furness and Lyth, North Morecambe Bay. *Publs Inst. Br. Geogr.* 25, 79–103.

HOLT, J. (1795). *General view of the agriculture of the County of Lancaster.* London.

HUGHES, D. O. and WALTERS, W. G. D. (1932). Soil Survey of Wales. Progress Report, 1929–1931. *Welsh J. Agric.* 8, 197–213.

HUGHES, D. O. and WALTERS, W. G. D. (1935). Soil Survey of Wales. Progress Report, 1931–1934. *Welsh J. Agric.* 11, 188–208.

KUBIENA, W. L. (1953). *The soils of Europe.* Murby, London.

METEOROLOGICAL OFFICE. (1952). *Climatological Atlas of the British Isles.* Sect. 3. M.O. 488. H.M.S.O.

METEOROLOGICAL OFFICE. (1958). *Averages of Rainfall.* M.O. 635.

METSON, A. J. (1956). *Methods of chemical analysis for soil survey samples.* Bull. Soil Bur. N.Z. 12.

PRUS-CHACINSKI, T. M. and HARRIS, W. B. (1963). Standards for lowland drainage and flood alleviation and drainage of peat lands, with special reference to the Crossens scheme. *Proc. Instn civ. Engrs.* 24, 177–206.

ROBERTS, I. (1871). Sections of the boulder clay at the Gasworks, Linacre, near Liverpool. *Proc. Lpool geol. Soc.* 1, 68.

RUSSELL, E. W. (1961). *Soil conditions and plant growth.* Longmans, London.

SOIL SURVEY STAFF. (1960). *Field Handbook.* Soil Survey of Great Britain.

U.S.D.A. (1951). *Soil Survey Manual.* United States Department of Agriculture.

WRAY, D. A. and COPE, F. W. (1948). *Geology of Southport and Formby.* Mem. geol. Surv. U.K.

Methods and Terms used in Profile Descriptions

To describe the properties of soil horizons, so that comparisons can be made between the horizons, the presentation of the information should be uniform. The methods and terms used in profile descriptions (Soil Survey Staff, 1960) are based, with slight modification, on those laid down in the U.S.D.A. Soil Survey Manual (1951). A summary of the more important features follows:

Depth and Clarity of Horizons

The depths to horizon boundaries are measured in inches from the surface of the mineral soil and the range of variation, if any, is noted. Boundaries are described as even, if nearly plane; undulating, if projections upward or downward are wider than their depth; or irregular, if deeper than their width.

The clarity of boundaries is described as sharp, if the transition is less than 1 in. wide; narrow if 1–2½ in. wide; merging, if the transition is more than 2½ in. wide.

Colour

In order to describe colours as objectively as possible, use is made of the Munsell Soil Color Chart designed for this purpose. According to the Munsell system of notation each colour may be considered as a resultant of three variables, hue, value and chroma*, designated in that order. Thus the hue 10 YR, the value 5 and the chroma 6 are combined to give the notation 10 YR 5/6. Colours with closely related notations are grouped under standard names; the colour name "yellowish brown", for example, covers the notations 10 YR 5/4, 10 YR 5/6 and 10 YR 5/8.

In recording soil colours in the field, the basic colour of a horizon is normally taken as that of a fresh surface in the moist condition, and if the colour changes markedly on drying the colour of the air-dry soil is also noted. Many soil horizons, particularly those which are incompletely weathered or subjected to seasonal waterlogging, are variegated with a pattern related to structural faces and root channels. The kind, contrast and distribution of the colours in such mottled horizons are described in standard terms.

Texture and stoniness

The term texture is commonly applied by agriculturalists to a complex of physical characteristics of the soil, including mechanical composition, structure, consistency and porosity, which influence ease of working, permeability, and water-holding capacity. In soil science "texture" refers specifically to the particle-size distribution, as obtained by standard methods of mechanical analysis, of the inorganic soil material which passes a 2 mm. sieve.

To determine the texture class in the field, some moistened soil is worked between finger and thumb until any aggregates are destroyed and a condition of maximum plasticity is attained. The soil is then assigned to a textural class according to the estimated proportions of sand (2·0–0·05 mm.), silt (0·05–0·002 mm.) and clay (<0·002

---

* The hue notation of a soil colour indicates its relation to the spectral colours yellow and red; the value notation indicates its lightness or brilliance; the chroma notation indicates its strength or departure from a neutral (black, grey or white) of the same value.

mm.) particle-size grades. In assessing the texture class of surface horizons, allowance has to be made for the influence of organic matter, significant amounts of which tend to make both sandy and clayey soils feel more silty.

Twelve basic textural classes are recognized, and Fig. 9 shows the range of particle-size distribution of each class. The basic class names may be modified by adjectival

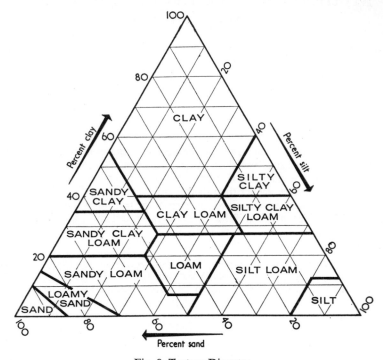

Fig. 9. Texture Diagram.

additions to indicate the dominant size-grade within the sand fraction (*e.g.* fine sandy loam; coarse sandy loam), the kind and quantity of stones (*e.g.* pebbly sand; stony loam), or the presence of more than about 13 per cent. of organic matter (*e.g.* humose loam; peaty clay loam).

In describing the stoniness of soil horizons, the following broad classes (by volume) are recognized:

few or occasional stones	.	<15 per cent.
stony . . .	.	15–20 per cent.
very stony. . .	.	>50 per cent.

Structure

Soil structure refers to the arrangement of primary soil particles into compound units or aggregates separated by voids or surfaces of weakness. The natural development of structure is influenced by the texture and physicochemical constitution of the soil material; by biological agencies, particularly soil fauna; and by seasonal wetting, drying and freezing. The structure of the surface soil is greatly affected by land use, and especially by cultivation which normally results in the disruption of natural soil aggregates or peds, accompanied by the fabrication of more or less transient, artificial structural units (clods). In loamy and clayey soils the structure of surface and sub-surface horizons largely determines their aeration and permeability and hence is of prime significance to crop growth.

Field descriptions of soil structure note the shape and arrangement, the average size, and the distinctness and durability of the structural units. Terms used to describe the shape and size are as follows:

1. Units with the vertical axis distinctly longer than the horizontal are sub-divided into: (*a*) *prismatic*, with flat or pointed tops, (*b*) *columnar*, with rounded tops, and are described according to their average width as fine (less than 2 cm.), medium (2–5 cm.) or coarse (more than 5 cm.).
2. Units with the horizontal axis longer than the vertical are described as *platy* or *laminated*.
3. Units with axes roughly equal are sub-divided into: (*a*) *blocky*, either angular or sub-angular, with distinct edges and smooth faces fitting closely together and are further described as fine (less than 1 cm.), medium (1–2 cm.), or coarse (more than 2 cm.), (*b*) *granular:* small (less than 1 cm.), rough-surfaced, irregular aggregates without distinct edges or faces; *crumb* is reserved for soft porous granular aggregates resembling bread-crumbs.

Many soil horizons have compound structures either of peds of different sizes, or of smaller peds held together as larger aggregates. Thus, many surface horizons contain both sub-angular blocky and granular peds (the latter often as worm casts or their residues), and fine-textured subsoil horizons frequently consist of large prisms which, when disturbed, break into distinct angular blocky peds.

The grade or degree of structure, representing the difference between cohesion within structural units and adhesion between them, varies with moisture content, and generally becomes more pronounced as the soil dries. In the field it is estimated by noting the distinctness of the structural units and the extent to which they are broken or destroyed when the soil mass is displaced or gently crushed. The following terms are used:

Structureless: no planes of weakness nor observable aggregation in either the moist or dry condition; massive if coherent; single-grain if non-coherent.

Weak: poorly formed, indistinct units which break easily on displacement, yielding much unaggregated or fragmental material.

Moderate: well formed, distinct units that are moderately resistant to disruption on disturbance.

Strong: well formed units, distinct in undisturbed moist soil, which adhere only weakly and can be separated without disruption when the soil is disturbed.

Consistence

Soil consistence comprises those attributes of soil material (commonly described by such terms as "heavy" and "light"), that are expressed by the degree and kind of cohesion and adhesion or by the resistance offered to deformation or rupture.

Consistence is closely related to both texture and structure, but whereas structure results from differences in the forces of attraction within a soil mass, consistence results from the strength and nature of the forces themselves.

Because consistence varies with moisture conditions, terms are needed for each significant moisture state: thus a ped or clod may be hard when dry, friable when moist*, plastic when wet†. The range of moisture content in which it is friable is an important characteristic affecting the workability of the soil. The following terms are used to describe consistence:

Loose: non-coherent when moist or dry.

Friable: when moist, crushes under gentle pressure, but coheres when pressed together.

---

* Referring specifically to a moisture content roughly mid-way between air-dry and field capacity.
† Referring specifically to a moisture content at or slightly above field capacity.

Firm: when moist crushes under moderate pressure, but resistance is distinctly noticeable; very firm soil materials are difficult to crush between finger and thumb.

Soft: weakly coherent and fragile when dry; breaks to powder or individual grains
under slight pressure.

Hard: when dry moderately resistant to pressure; can be broken in the hands but is
barely breakable between finger and thumb; very hard soil materials can be broken
in the hands only with difficulty.

Indurated: brittle and hard at all moisture contents.

Compact: denotes a combination of firm consistence and close packing or arrangement
of particles.

Plastic: when wet, retains an impressed shape and can be moulded into a wire or thin
rod without disruption; very plastic soil materials require much pressure for deformation, and are normally of fine texture.

Porosity and Permeability

When a profile is examined by eye, small pores, within the structural aggregates, and
fissures, between aggregates, are apparent. Fissures and pores are described in terms of
quantity (*e.g.* common, 10–100 per square decimeter) and size (*e.g.* medium fissures,
3–5 mm. wide; medium pores, 1–3 mm. in diameter) and their main direction and
pattern of distribution is indicated.

Soil permeability is that quality of the soil which permits it to transmit water or air.
It can be measured in terms of percolation rates under specified conditions, but in the
absence of precise measurements soil horizons may be placed in relative permeability
classes by studies of structure, texture, porosity, arrangement of fissures and other
observable characteristics. Rate of permeability is described as slow, moderate or rapid
and is a property of the horizon as a whole and not only of individual aggregates.
Permeability tends to vary seasonally, especially in the case of clay soils which may be
well fissured after frosty weather or a long dry period.

Soil Organic Matter

Organic matter occurs in various forms and positions in soil profiles. It occurs as
surface accumulations, or mixed with mineral matter, or as concentrations in essentially
mineral horizons.

Surface accumulations of organic matter are either described as peat, where the
profile consists of a considerable thickness of organic matter or as *mor* or *moder* when
referring to distinct layers of organic matter on the surface of mineral soils.

Descriptions of peat include the recognition of its botanical composition, the degree
of humification and the structural properties. The structure of organic soils is described
in the same terms as mineral soils but the structure of peat is described as either fibrous,
pseudo-fibrous or amorphous, depending on the presence or absence of recognizable
plant remains. In terms of von Post's scale of humification, peat can be described as
slightly humified (H1–H5), moderately humified (H6–H7) or strongly humified (H8–
H10). When squeezed in the hand, little more than dy-charged water escapes between
the fingers if humification is slight. Up to about two-thirds of the mass of moderately
humified peat can be squeezed between the fingers while practically all can be so
extruded from strongly humified peat.

Thin surface accumulations of organic matter are described as *mor* or *moder* and the
component litter (L layer), fermentation (F layer) and humification layers (H layer) are
treated as normal soil horizons. In mor or raw humus the L and F layers are strongly
developed and the H layer is thin and sharply separated from the mineral soil. Moder is
a mixture of organic matter and mineral particles that can be separated mechanically
and is commonly found on sandy soils. Thoroughly humified organic matter forming
clay-humus complexes is described as *mull* and is a common constituent of agricultural
soils.

Mixed mineral and organic matter and concentrations of organic matter in mainly mineral horizons are described in terms of organic-matter content (*e.g.* very high, more than 13 per cent.; low, less than 3 per cent.), the kind of organic matter and its distribution.

Roots and Fauna

Roots are described in terms of quantity, size, kinds, nature and condition. The relationships of roots to other soil characters such as structure and water-table are also indicated.

Soil fauna are described and the recognition of casts and burrows, for example, is an important part of soil description.

Concentrations mainly of Pedogenic Origin

Concentrations of mineral materials arising mainly as a result of the process of soil formation are described in terms of form (*e.g.* efflorescences, crusts, dendrites, veins, tubes, streaks, interlayers or coatings), abundance and chemical composition. Such concentrations commonly consist of calcium carbonate and compounds of iron and manganese.

Soil-drainage Classes

Drainage, as a condition of the soil, refers to the frequency and duration of periods when the profile is wholly or partly saturated with water. It is determined by the rapidity and extent of removal of water by surface run-off (external drainage) and by the downward percolation (internal drainage), by the balance of rainfall and evaporation, and by the proximity of subterranean zones of permanent saturation.

Soil drainage may be assessed in the field by inference from relief and profile morphology, coupled with observations of moisture conditions at different periods of the year. In making the assessment, emphasis is placed on the presence and intensity of mottling and/or grey colours produced by gleying at different levels in the profile, and it is assumed that these effects afford valid comparative indications of differing drainage in profiles of similar constitution. Thus, permanently waterlogged soil horizons are normally pale grey in colour, depending on the extent to which ferrous compounds have been removed by seepage or accumulated *in situ*, whereas periodically waterlogged horizons are characteristically variegated with ochreous and greyish mottlings, which more or less mask inherited colours and form a pattern related to structural faces and root channels. In interpreting these morphological features, it must be recognized that organic reducing agents are necessary for gleying to occur, and that the colour effects produced vary greatly with the amount and nature of the iron-bearing minerals. Iron is probably mobilized more readily at lower pH values, so that the effects may be less marked in calcareous soils than in acid soils of similar texture and drainage status. Furthermore, where drainage has been improved, either naturally or artificially, the profile may still show features, such as rust stains and mottles, indicative of its former condition. It is therefore necessary, particularly when dealing with agricultural soils, to use all available evidence, and to avoid placing undue reliance on morphological features that may be unrelated to the contemporary drainage status of the soil.

On the basis of such observations it is possible to distinguish a sequence of drainage classes and definitions of the five recognized in this memoir are given below:

Excessively drained: water is removed from the soil rapidly, and the amount retained is such that growth of crop plants is severely limited by drought in most seasons; the soil is often loose or very friable, has a low earthworm population, and may have a high content of organic matter. This class includes shallow soils over hard rock, often on steep slopes, and soils developed on very porous, coarse-textured materials.

Freely drained: water is removed from the soil readily but sufficient is retained to allow normal growth of crops and grass except in drought periods. Freely drained soils are normally deep and free of mottling throughout the profile (or to at least three feet); they are usually coarse to medium textured, but some fine-textured soils with pervious substrata are included.

Imperfectly drained: water is removed from the soil slowly, so that parts of the root zone remain saturated for significant periods in most seasons but permanent waterlogging occurs only at depths below about 24 in. Imperfectly drained soils typically show distinct ochreous and/or pale-coloured mottling below about 12 in.

Poorly drained: water is removed from the soil so slowly that the root zone remains saturated for a considerable part of the year, and permanent waterlogging may occur below about 18 in. Poorly drained soils normally show pronounced ochreous and/or grey mottling throughout the profile. Artificial drainage is necessary for satisfactory crop production and semi-natural vegetation includes hydrophilous species.

Very poorly drained: the soil remains more or less permanently saturated with water, and semi-natural vegetation is of a markedly hydrophilous character. Soils of this class normally have highly organic surface horizons overlying a grey mineral subsoil with or without ochreous mottling.

Index

Six figure National Grid References are given in parenthesis after place names; grid letters are SD unless otherwise stated.